CU00658265

For Jonny, who is really a fox,
but who asked for a book, and who always looks up.

Published by Little Toller Books in 2021
Little Toller Books, Ford, Pineapple Lane, Dorset

Typeset in Caslon and Perpetua by Little Toller Books

Printed by TJ Books, Padstow, Cornwall

All papers used by Little Toller Books are natural, recyclable products made from wood grown in sustainable, well-managed forests

A catalogue record for this book is available from the British Library

ISBN 978-1-908213-84-6

1

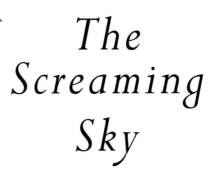

The
Screaming
Sky

CHARLES FOSTER

Illustrated by
Jonathan Pomroy

A LITTLE TOLLER **MONOGRAPH**

… [B]ecause we share both some ancestry and many sensory modalities with birds, it is just possible that we share a common emotionality …

TIM BIRKHEAD, *Bird Sense*

All names fall short of the shining of things

PETER MATTHIESSEN, *The Snow Leopard*

Contents

July 17th swifts approaching eaves

Jonathan Pomroy

Author's Note

This is the account of an obsession.

There are probably worse obsessions than an obsession with swifts, but there are no doubt better ones too.

Because it is the account of an obsession, by the obsessive, there is inevitably something of me in it, taking up space that might have been used for more information about swifts.

There are thought to be about 18,000 bird species on the planet. How can a whole book about just one be justified?

Surely what needs to be justified is the *absence* of books about most other species. Each and every species on earth deserves an infinity of books. Every one is infinitely complex and wonderful, and the life of every one is intimately interwoven with the life of everything else.

So I don't think I need an *excuse* for writing this book. But perhaps I should explain that one of the reasons for my monomania is that swifts have been a gateway to places more obviously connected with human thriving than a nestbox nailed under the eaves. Swifts have taught me a lot of the little I know about how to be a father, a friend and a human. That, on the face of it, is odd. I explore the oddness in this book. And I do use the sun that shines through the wings of a swooping swift to shed light on some general questions about our way of being in the world.

I need to declare my conviction that we can only get at the general through the particular. That, being small, discrete, local, embodied animals, we have to start our search for overarching principles in small, discrete, local, embodied ways. I'm encouraged that the best travel books are written by authors who know one place really well; that the best books about relationships are written not by people who wake up in a different bed each morning, but by those who have worked hard and long at one relationship; that the really impressive polyglots inhabit one language particularly.

This is not a scientific book, but I have tried to get the science right. If you're trying to spell out the poetry in the graphs and charts and equations you won't get very far if you've misread the articles. There are still many exhilarating uncertainties in swift biology. Long may it continue – and I'm sure it will.

There are some numbers and calculations. If you don't like that sort of thing, skip them. Inconsistently, but I hope helpfully, I've used imperial units for distance and metric units for weight.

It's usual for monographs about animals to be divided into chapters on reproduction, nutrition, migration, predation, threats and so on. I see the sense of that, but it makes me uneasy. For those are human categories. Squeezing an animal inside them is a kind of colonialism. Each animal has one life, flowing constantly through time and space, affected at every moment by all the forces represented by the categories. It seemed to me that the least unsatisfactory way to reflect this continuity was to go through the year with the swifts. For swifts do, in a way, simply occupy January in a way that they do not merely, simply, contextlessly reproduce, migrate or die.

It seemed important, too, not to start the book in the European summer, which is when most of us experience swifts. For the breeding season is only three months of their year, and to lead with that would have given the impression that they are European birds; *our* birds. It would have been another bit of colonialism.

I didn't want to clutter up the text with explicit references to the scientific literature I've relied on, and so at the end of the book there's a section of notes which refer to the relevant page numbers of the book. The notes will let you see the authority for a few of the main assertions and arguments – those that I thought would be most controversial, and those that I thought readers would want to read more about.

There are 112 species of swift in the family *Apodidae,* across 18 genera. There are a further four species of treeswifts, in their own family and their own genus. This book deals only with the common swift, *Apus apus,* familiar to anyone in most of Europe and much of Asia who looks up in the summer, and to anyone in sub-Saharan Africa who looks up between September and April.

The word 'sky' appears here far too often, but since that's where swifts live, I couldn't avoid it.

I've changed some times, places, and personalities. You'll search Oxford in vain for the ex-friend.

C. F.
Oxford, 2021

January

It is always summer for them.

They're round my head now. One pulls away from my right ear with the tilt of a black wing, snatching at a fly that erupted this afternoon from the dung of a lion. Always at *a* fly: not at *flies*. They hunt, they don't trawl. They kill individuals. They have millions of intense experiences of the particular. Each experience chases the one before it, as swifts chase flies, in the hurtling stream of life in the sky.

As the fly slid over the back of the hard triangular tongue, where the taste buds are irrigated by the salivary ducts, the bird tasted lion musk on the thorax. Flies only stop being individuals and become paste when they're squashed together in the throat pouch, and since these swifts aren't feeding young, the pouches are empty in Africa, and each fly goes straight down.

My paunch is rarely empty. In Africa, right now, swollen under my sticky khaki shirt, it is full of yam and snake, awash in fizzy Laurentina beer which takes the edge off the homesickness.

I can't remember the last time I experienced anything *particular* and *concrete*. Everything's generic and abstract for me. My world's made of words and my own wretched ideas. These birds don't fly through their idea of the sky: they fly through the sky. They eat flies, not a collection of adjectives for describing flies. They have no words to separate them from the sun that rose out of Madagascar this morning, from the monkeys picking out their friends' lice on the beach, from the crabs hiding under the mangroves from the herons, from the elephants in baggy trousers crashing through the mahogany trees behind me.

I have been sitting here for three hours now, looking out to sea through a fug of heavy air; air thrashing with metallic insect legs. I've moved my hand to lift the beer to my mouth, and to pull my hat over my eyes, and my boots have cut furrows in the red earth under the table, and my blood cells must have done a few miles as they've squeezed through the tubes, dumping oxygen into my cells and engulfing the malaria parasites.

In that time the swift by my ear might easily have flown a hundred miles or more over the bush. It might have killed a thousand times, have buzzed a Panamanian freighter on the run from Somali pirates, have seen hyenas running down an ailing giraffe, have coughed on the fumes blown north from Maputo, reunited joyously with the mate it last saw under the eaves of a terraced house in Oxford, dodged the shot of a bored villager, mocked a falcon that thought for an absurd moment that it might snatch the swift and eat its liver, and *played* – because not everything is about the algorithms of survival.

That's a lot of living in three hours. The swift might be

twenty-one years old. Twenty-one years of a life like that makes me ashamed to be me. It's like comparing a symphony with a burp of white noise.

Another bottle of Laurentina is now sloshing round with the snake, and the throbbing heat is pressing on me, making me feel as if I were face down on my own wet thighs. I'm breathing great lungfuls of midges and some of them stick in my teeth and I wash them down with beer, and the woman who sails towards me like a galleon in spotted yellow cotton bearing the beer on her foredeck shouts: 'It's coming soon, m'darling.'

It did. It came in from the north-west. It had risen high up over the dark forest of the Democratic Republic of the Congo, bundling bugs and spiders up with it, and it growled over Malawi, starting to splutter as it crossed the border into Mozambique.

The swifts had known for hours that the cyclone was coming because they had spiralled high that morning on an early thermal and seen it gathering, and because they felt the thrum of its heart shiver through their own tiny chests. They could pick up infrasound across half a continent. They knew the sound of grinding tectonic plates, mourning elephants and dyspeptic mountains.

They flirt round the cyclone's edge, grazing on floundering spiders which had tried to spin silk around drops of rain blown at the speed of an express train. They're careful not to be sucked into the churning belly: it would rip off their wings, pluck off their feathers and spit them into the sea somewhere near Mauritius.

I lean against a doorpost, watching a curtain of rain pour from the thatch, as heavy and dense as those bead curtains in Chinese restaurants. The weather is charging back out to sea. There it will collide with the trade winds gusting up from the south-east, and they will negotiate, and for a while warm rain will spatter on the sea, and the lemurs of Madagascar will dance in the puddles.

Swifts aren't particularly early risers. They don't see any point in getting up before the insects. But the next morning they are up long before me, and by the time I stumble out onto the veranda, rubbing my eyes, they're all full. But they carry on killing, forcing each struggler down. Africa, for all its bounteousness, is fickle, and they can't be sure that it will keep on giving.

They're hunting low now, never more than a hundred yards above the ground, cutting into the territory of the swallows and the martins who are usually below them. The rains have filled the air with insect bodies, and the sun's not yet hot enough to waft them to the tree-tops and beyond, where the martins don't bother to challenge.

The swifts are too high-octane for this kind of hunting. For cornering, stalling and snatching you want stubbier wings and more aerobatic tails. The swallows do it well, weaving between the knickers on the washing lines, threading through the windows of a bankrupt bordello, almost but not quite touching the grass heads with their wing tips, perching on a telephone wire (through which terrible news was coming) to discuss, digest and draw breath. They are land creatures who can fly. The swifts are not. They inhabit the air as fish inhabit the sea. They don't perch to draw breath. I feel that they're like some sharks, who will drown if they're forced to stop moving forwards, for water needs to flow constantly over their gills. Swifts' devotion to the air and to movement is like that.

The swifts that hatch in the eaves a few feet above my head in Oxford might well come to northern Mozambique and back to Oxford four times before touching anything more solid than the carapace of an airborne beetle. Only when they breed will they, for three months, enter for a while, and intermittently, the gross, crass world of solids – the only one we know, apart from our brief wallowings in water. If they don't find someone to settle down with they might never know that world at all.

I mustn't overstate the case. While it is fashionable and romantic to say that non-breeding swifts don't land, most of them sometimes do – but for only about one per cent of the time, and then perhaps only when faced with dangerously forbidding weather. Landing is probably more common in young migrating birds. Who can blame them?

Yesterday I took a boat across to an island which bristled with rusty cannon. We wove between the dugongs, waded ashore onto the crystalline sand, climbed through the remnants of a wall felled by a falling tree, and wandered into the old slaving citadel. A bald dog raised its head on a rococo veranda, and laid it down again. Ants had eaten the wooden pegs tacking the cross to the church, and it hung blasphemously upside down. The tree outside the church, planted to shade Portuguese ladies, just absolved of their adulteries, chittered with weaver birds.

A six-year-old kid, covered in boils, beckoned me urgently over. I followed him into the churchyard. He took my hand and pulled me down into a crumbling vault. Many of the graves had been smashed, and the termites had got to the coffins. The boy reached into a grave, pulled out a human femur, and offered it to me. I shook my head. He reached in again, and pulled out a skull. This time I took it. It seemed rude not to. There was a hole in the side of the skull. Not even a blackened scrap of brain or muscle remained. All the soft bits of this mid-nineteenth-century slave-trader had been made into insects and rats, and those insects and rats had been made into birds. Some of those birds might well have found their way back to Portugal, though the man did not.

I held up the skull. The empty orbits had held eyes which swivelled to watch swifts screaming round the porticos and chimney stacks of Lisbon. For some of his journey to Africa he'd have taken more or less the same route as those swifts. His ship would have crept down the coast of Morocco, Western Sahara, Mauritania and Senegal. While off Senegal he'd have had his first noseful of the stewed vegetableness of tropical Africa, and then the ship would have curled slowly eastwards into the Gulf of Guinea. He'd have stopped there for water, going nervously through the surf in an outrigger canoe, trying to forget the tales of crucifixion and cannibalism.

The mid-nineteenth-century swifts flew over the land to feed, but never far from the surf. They then cut inland through the Congo forest, while the slave-trader sailed on south, round the Cape of Good Hope, to rejoin the swifts in Mozambique.

If the slave-trader had gone to Mozambique to escape the

ghosts of Lisbon, the swifts would have reminded him that there was no escape: that the world is one place. If he ever went back home to Lisbon in the summer, hoping to forget the obscenities he'd committed for his masters, the swifts would be there, making escape impossible. Swifts, if we see them properly, always confront us with ourselves, and the confrontation is not pleasant.

Last night, sweating under my mosquito net, I'd done some depressing calculations on the back of a menu. From Oxford to Mozambique (I'd calculated, increasingly moodily) is around 6,000 miles. The swifts do that journey twice a year. In the autumn it takes them around 66 days: 30 days travelling and 36 days of stopovers, when they browse rather cursorily, as we'd pick at a bag of crisps at a motorway service station. In the spring they're in much more of a hurry. It takes them around 26 days, of which 21 are strenuous mile-eating days, and 5 are stopovers. I allowed them (conservatively) 70 miles of flying per stopover day, and assumed that they flew 80 miles per day during the winter, and the menu looked like this:

Autumn migration:
6,000 miles plus 36 stopover days (36 days x 70 miles)
= 8,520 miles.

Spring migration:
6,000 miles plus 5 stopover days (5 days x 70 miles)
= 6,350 miles.

Non-migration days:
273 days x 80 miles = 21,840 miles.

Annual total: 36,710 miles.
Swifts are known to live for up to 21 years.
21 years x 36,710 miles = 770,910 miles.

That's 3.23 trips to the moon, or 1/121 of a trip to the sun.

These are literally astronomical birds (I didn't write on the menu).

And then I turned to myself.

If I walked a respectable 20 miles a day every day of the year, it would take me over five years to cover what the swifts do in one. If I wanted to match the lifetime total of that twenty-one-year-old swift, I'd have to start walking 20 miles a day on the day of my birth, and carry on doing it for 106 years. (As we'll see, young swifts start flying epic distances not long after they hatch).

I don't come well out of this.

I count up the number of species whose corpses, stems, flowers, roots or seeds I've eaten this week. It has been a pretty catholic week, but still I can't get beyond two species of mammal, a reptile, two bird species, three types of tubers, two types of nut, one species of modified flower and two types of modified grass. That's thirteen species in all. Over the course of a year my plate gets occasional guest appearances, and I might push the total to twenty. Just three species – rice, maize and wheat – are the staples of three-quarters of modern humans.

Swifts prey on around five hundred different species. They're highly selective feeders: indiscriminate suction traps catch a far higher proportion of flies than appears in swift diets from the same area. Swifts' fastidiousness may mean that they *distinguish* five hundred species. They're not just identifying succulent *types,* or veering away from insects with warning colouration. When they're hunting bees, they take the stingless drones, yellow-and-black-banded though they are, and leave the stingers. And they distinguish the species not, as we do, after peering at them through a hand lens when they're pinned out on a cork board, or after a leisurely look through binoculars in a heated hide, but when they're hurtling towards them, perhaps at 50 miles an hour, with the wind smashing into their faces. How many bird species can a really expert ornithologist confidently recognise in a fleeting glimpse – recognise by the 'jizz' – by the intuition that bypasses reason but is built on experience? Perhaps a hundred?

I don't grow or kill much of my own food at all. I delegate it to others. I kill by proxy, and, unlike the swifts, kill when it is unnecessary. I think myself fine, involved and engaged if I make a loaf of bread from wheat grown in Canada, yeast cultured in a Scottish factory, and water treated and pumped to me through pipes made of Papuan copper, and bake it using heat from a Mesozoic swamp somewhere under Arabia. I eat my food, usually, sitting at a table, looking at the same wall I've looked at for the last ten years. One fifth of all meals in the USA are eaten in a car. Except when they're nestlings, all swift meals are eaten in the sky – sky to which they've taken themselves, sky which they've never been in before, and never will be again (for the sky, like rivers, flows all the time).

They bathe by diving through a cloud or vibrating their wings in the rain that has just dropped out of the cloud. I bathe by turning on a tap and soaking in a tub of dilute chlorine and female reproductive hormones. They cool down as they fly by opening their mouths to increase evaporation, and by dangling their naked, scaly feet below their bodies. I cool down by flicking a switch and raiding the fridge. Self-esteem is hard when you look at swifts.

*

In the sparse non-scientific literature on swifts there are many themes. One is *aspiration*. We want to be like them, say the aspirants; we're *meant* to be like them. If we play our theological cards right we *will* be like them one day. Follow them and we'll wash off the crud that besoils us. They're literally ethereal, and our souls, being ethereal too, want to play with the swifts rather than with X-boxes or middle-managers or sociopathic leaders.

> … [W]hen eve shines slowly
> And the light is thinned,
> And the moon slides slowly
> Down the far-off wind …

So wrote Wilfred Owen, one of the aspirants.

> O, then to be of all the birds the swift!
> To flit through ether, with elves winging …
> thy spirit's tirelessness I crave;
> Yet more thy joyous fierce endurance.

Janet Andrews developed multiple sclerosis as a young woman. By her 60s she had only slight movement in one arm and hand, and couldn't get up without the help of her carers and a mechanical hoist. Her beloved swifts moved for her. 'The swifts are back', she wrote. 'Scything through the air on outstretched wings, they cross the heavens, oblivious of us, earthbound so far beneath. They bring the summer with them. I feel their energy. I am amazed by their innate skill, their beauty. Oh to be up there with them, looking down on our ordinary lives.'

Well, yes. But I am affronted by the dismissive attention of those button-black eyes, looking unblinkingly down at me –

always down – from the high blue and the high moral ground.

We can't deal with swifts. They won't play our games. That makes them terribly important. 'It is the things that ignore us that save us in the end', wrote Andrew Harvey. I'd want to add some footnotes to that, but it's not a bad first principle. If we respond to disdain, cruelty, inattention or anything with wonder, kindness and attention, we're on the road to salvation.

We don't usually respond that way. For those who notice the birds at all, most are threatened by them (as they should be), and cope with the threat by trying to domesticate or denigrate.

The domesticators are always nice people. 'Say hello to my swifts for me, will you?' asked one of them, when he heard that I was off to Africa in the winter. 'I miss them.' I've no doubt he does. He's screwed swift nestboxes onto his house, and bought a CD of swift screams to try to entice swifts to nest there. He's got a shelf of swift books, a stuffed swift in a glass dome, and some of those stiff nineteenth-century lithographs of perching, anatomically impossible swifts in his hall. Yet these are artefacts not of devotion, but of control. Aslan wasn't a tame lion. Swifts are not tame birds. Tame them, and they stop being swifts, and if they're not swifts they can't help us.

'These are not *your* swifts,' I want to shout. 'Not yours: not mine: not anyone's. They are their own, as very few humans are their own.'

He'd be hurt and outraged. He's happy when the swifts come to his boxes. It makes the sky, to which we'll all one day return, and which is where the swifts belong, shrink down to a manageable size (35 cm x 20 cm x 180 cm, to be exact, because he's got deep soffits). If that's the size of the heavens, there's nothing to fear either in life or death, and you really can believe that you're the sovereign of the universe. Swifts are safe if they're penned inside a glass dome or a picture frame, and safer still if they're petrified and sclerosed as they were in the hands of those Victorian lithographers.

Am I being uncharitable? Possibly. But imprisoning wild things, even if it's only in your mind, is a serious offence. Imprisoning the *wild* and potting the billowing heavens is even worse. And using the wild for one's own aggrandisement and psychotherapy is worse still. It's a kind of canned hunting.

There are more nuanced and still more dangerous strategies of domestication. Some try to lock swifts up inside language. It never works: swifts are far too fast to be snared by words. The danger is in the hubris of the attempt. 'And the swift flicked through the breath of a violet', Ted Hughes tells us. To my certain knowledge no swift has ever done that. Swifts spin 'life's thread/As you have done for generations', writes Randle Manwaring. 'Favouring old houses and towers/At Sant' Antonio and Sant' Quirico.' No: swifts don't spin life's thread as we have done. They have a wholly different way of being. Old houses and towers don't do them a favour. They do old houses and towers a favour by condescending to live there. Don't patronise.

Swifts are engaged, says Hugh David Loxdale, in

> … [A] perennial struggle
> To feed, reproduce
> And fly free again.
> One that, maybe, will never end –
> Assuming the Spring and they return
> Year after year
> Long into the unimagined future.
> Beyond human strife and bombs,
> So that this most joyous scene shall remain.

The swifts in full chase or play,
A certainty, a must.
Each May
And on into August …

Why do you want the swifts, Mr Loxdale? To reassure you that the world is still turning smoothly, so that you can get on with your life?

Why does Hughes so famously exult in swifts? Why is he glad that they're back? Because it means that 'the globe's still working, the Creation's/Still waking refreshed, our summer's/Still all to come – '. The swifts are sedatives: CBT counsellors. They're about *him,* not about themselves. He covers his tracks well, but there's one dead give-away: that distinct proprietorial note: '*our* summer'. Under the breathless adjectivising is the old Neolithic mandate, codified in Genesis and later misconstrued catastrophically: subdue the earth; it exists for Hughes and his conspecifics. If it weren't for the obvious and abject failure of the poems, they'd be deadly for the poets, their readers and the planet. 'Nought out of ten', screech the swifts as they hurtle by beyond sight, thought and syntax, saving from themselves those who can hear them.

If the swifts can't be caged (and they can't), the humans who notice them have other coping strategies. The main one is denigration. It's often used in addition to the attempts at domestication – often, indeed, in the same breath. What are they to Hughes, other than therapists? They're yobs. They roar away 'On a steep/Controlled scream of skid'. They erupt across the yard: 'Shrapnel-scatter terror. Frog-gapers, Speedway goggles, international mobsters … On their switchback wheel of death'. Their flight is a 'lunatic limber scramming frenzy', and a grounded fledgling is a 'moustachioed goblin savage'.

For Anne Collie, a swift is 'a machine for flying, with an evil eye/Glaring in vicious anger', and many writers reach for martial or diabolical words. Swift wings are scimitar blades 'slashing/Rents in summer skies', 'cleaving the still air' as the swifts 'come to distribute death'. 'For sure they are Satan's cherubim … Fizzing past like hot shrapnel. You can see their demonic, glittering little faces./Their wings sound like whips/Their screams tear the fabric of this world', and who can plumb (and who would want to plumb) 'The black depths of their devil thoughts'? To W. H. Hudson they are possessed by fury, 'tormented beings … like those doomed wretches in the halls of Eblis, whose hearts were in a blaze of unquenchable fire, and who, every one with hands pressed to his chest, went spinning round in an everlasting, agonised dance.' Even for the gentle John Clare the swift is the 'develing black as coal'.

The swifts slice through the slander as they slice through the air. None of it sticks. It just makes the slanderers sound stuttering and sad. As swifts are faster than thought and word and human deed, so they are bigger than our ideas. 'All reality is iconoclastic', wrote C. S. Lewis. 'The earthly beloved, even in this life, continually triumphs over your mere idea of her.' And swifts are very real indeed, and so they mince (there, I'm making them violent now) our dowdy pedestrian ideas of them.

To follow the swifts turns out to be an education in not-knowing. It's an ancient, crucial and forgotten skill. It makes it rather difficult to write a book about swifts, mind you, for books are supposed to be *about* something, to move us on, to fill us up, not to compound and celebrate our ignorance, and assert the absurdity of assertion.

There are two ways of right unknowing. There is the way

of intuition. That was R. S. Thomas's way. He stared up, more or less unencumbered by ornithological data, and understood:

> There is no solving the problem
> [Swifts] pose …
> I am learning to bring
> Only my wonder to the contemplation
> Of the geometry of their dark wings.

And there is the way of shuffling, slippered, cocoa-sipping, cosy love and familiarity, which takes us, in the end, to the same place as the mystics. Here is the mild eighteenth-century clergyman Gilbert White, he who thought that swallows hibernated at the bottom of ponds, and who was the first to distinguish between the chiffchaff and the willow warbler, writing in his careful copperplate about the mysterious swifts that 'dash(ed) round the steeple' of his Selborne church:

> To mark the swift in rapid giddy ring. …
> Unsubdued of wing.
> Amusive birds! -say where your hid retreat
> When the frost rages and the tempests beat;
> Whence your return, by such nice instinct led,
> When spring, soft season, lifts her bloomy head?
> Such baffled searches mock men's prying pride,
> The God of Nature is your secret guide! …

It's notionally an expression of scientific frustration. He's been worrying away for years at the conundrums of migration. Where do they go? Why do they go? How do they go? He's got nowhere. And nowhere, as the swifts (as citizens of Nowhere) teach us, is the most respectable address of all. He's got nothing, which is the most valuable possession of all. And so, his prying pride having been roundly mocked by the squally night-squeals from the thick air around the belfries, he's back to R. S. Thomas's wonder.

This isn't defeat or despair; not the capitulation of rationalism to the inchoate forces of unreason. It's reason acknowledging, very rationally, where it can't go. We can tie harnesses onto swifts, and clip on light-level geolocators and plot their movements on the screen, and we can sequence their DNA and note their close affiliation with hummingbirds, and if anything it will diminish our real knowledge of swifts.

It's evening. I am high on a ridge looking to the sea on one side and, on the other, the howling, creeping interior of Africa, the Africa from which we all came: mottled, inconstant and, in the long run, kind. I've doused myself in chemicals to stop insect bites, and they make me wheeze. Bats the size of terriers, greasy black leather stretched between their fingertips, are starting to patrol and sniff for fruit. The land is starting to stir, to shake off the day's heat, to rustle, undulate, shine and purr. Soon it will crunch and moan, and the sea too will shudder awake and start to snap.

A strangled trumpeting and thrashing from the foot of the hill might mean that an elephant has put its foot in a snare, and that the snare is slicing into it like wire into soft cheese, and I fancy that I can smell the despair and the impotence of the other elephants. If they leave it, lions and hyenas will make short work of it. The poachers laid the snare for smaller game, but they know very well where to sell the tusks.

Swifts know the roar of lions better than the roar of the M25, the piping of hornbills better than the Nunc Dimittis of parish Evensong, giraffe better than cats, the centre of a cloud better than a fibreglass-lined hole in a suburban street. They're only in Oxford briefly and functionally. Mate, lay, brood, feed, go. A production line. Wham bam thank you Europe: you've got long days and intermittently good flies, but that's it. They've no time to connect with us, even if they had the inclination. We might feel connected to them because we can hear them rustling in our eaves. They don't feel the same.

But if I'm good; if I think nice thoughts and make standing orders to worthy charities; if I'm patient with hapless apparatchiks, and if I run the school jumble sale, perhaps the swifts will deign to come down from the shining heavens and show themselves – no, I want the old word, *vouchsafe* themselves – to this dirty, lumpen, earthbound mortal.

The pledge is enough! Here they are, carving the curd of the air so that it falls apart in slices behind them, swooshing north-west, curling up and away, always away.

It is time to head back, while I can still see snakes on the path. The swifts will be back tomorrow.

They weren't. Nor the next day, nor the day or the week after. There were plenty of tantalising imitators (nine species of swift and two species of spinetail have been recorded in Mozambique). I rejoice in African palm swifts, white-rumped swifts and Böhm's spinetails, but they're not *mine:* not the common swift, which is the least common thing, though there are 95–165 million of them on – or rather above – the planet.

And there we are: *'Mine'*. I'm at least as guilty of toxic proprietorship as the kindly, tweedy swift-box man I've been so cruel about. At least he's useful to swifts.

February

I stay around for a while, diverted for a time by palm swifts and leopards with tails dangling like toilet chains from trees, and Laurentina, and a snake oozing out of the foramen magnum of a wildebeest skull, and a rabid jackal, and a storm that dumped fish into the trees behind the house, and a curse on the village schoolmaster (for harsh marking of a maths exam) which ossified his ankles and knees and turned his tongue black, and lots of Dickens and Walter Scott, and a stupid overdose of salt tablets which kept me kneeling over a plastic bucket while the fish were raining down.

But I can't concentrate long on any of this. The sky draws me up, and the palm swifts tantalise. Every evening I go up to the ridge with my binoculars to stare into Africa and wonder where the common swifts are.

Once I thought I'd seen them, spurting out of a faraway rumble and flash to the north-west, and went back to my table under the bougainvillea feeling blessed. But the beer diluted my confidence. Were the wings too broad? The bodies too thin? The aerobatics insufficiently swashbuckling?

Once a week I go to the internet café to sit in a sticky plywood box, get news from Oxford and look at the weather maps for central Africa.

The troubling news from Oxford is that, although the gutters are plugged with snow, starlings are already looking interested in the swift eaves. They'll have finished breeding by the time the swifts arrive, I tell myself, knowing that it might well be untrue. I'm furious. It seems sacrilegious for such loud, coarse birds to muscle in on the swifts. It becomes *morally* important to stop them, and I bark instructions onto the keyboard – buy chicken wire; cut a square, 1 foot by 1 foot; scrumple it up; lean backwards out of the study window, trying not to fall; you'll see a hole just to the right of the window; shove the ball of wire into the hole; if you can secure it with staples, all the better; then we'll unplug it in the last week of April, hoping that the starlings won't be interested in a second brood by then.

And the troubling news for Africa is about some meteorological indices that I've followed for years when better fathers followed their children's school reports and more balanced men followed the football results.

Swift survival is generally very high (estimates vary between around 76–81 per cent every year), but one of the things that can reduce survival is an unusually cold Pacific current which moves big chunks of weather around in south and south-east Asia and Australasia, shunting blocks of rain over south-eastern Africa. This cold current is called La Niña, and those of us who fear it look nervously at the Oceanic Niño Index (ONI), which is based on anomalies in sea-surface temperatures and tells of the El Niño-Southern Oscillation (ENSO). These curt bureaucratic acronyms are the names of apocalyptic horsemen.

In a La Niña year there will be drought in East Africa: cows will die, vultures will bloat, and desperate human populations will clash in the Rift Valley.

Here in the south-east there will be floods. Mole-rats and elephant shrews will drown. Snakes will swim into bedrooms.

It doesn't look so dramatic for the swifts. They won't plummet exhausted from the sky. The drops won't batter them to the ground. If you wade through the brown water racing down a Maputo street you won't see their wasted bodies being washed away with the rats. But next summer, in Dorset, they'll say that it's a bad year for swifts, though it's a balmy June there.

No one knows why the swifts are so vulnerable. They've got all Africa to hunt in. They can see the rains coming from a long way off, and can fly faster than the rain. Often they waltz insolently with storms. My own theory is that they are mesmerised by the slow writhing of these cold storms as songbirds are said to be mesmerised by the dancing of stoats, and come near to gaze, and are inhaled and chilled to sleep.

This is a La Niña year, the forecasters insistently say. I feel vaguely responsible, and send another idiotic email about chicken wire.

The swifts from our Oxford roof might have been the ones I saw the other day. British swifts (no, I know that they're not British swifts, but the offensive shorthand's unavoidable) wander widely throughout the Congo Basin and into south-eastern Africa.

If the birds I saw in the Quirimbas carry on north-westwards, they'll cross Lake Malawi, ride the thermals bouncing off the steep slopes of the Mpui hills, and follow Lake Tanganyika northwards, dropping low to the surface of the lake to skim up mouthfuls of water and to harvest the insect hatchlings, just popping through the surface tension, which escaped the cichlids.

I think they'll pause here, fattening, before pushing on across the border into the DRC, looking down on trees boiling up like dark broccoli, brown rivers coiling back on themselves, little forest elephants whose hard ivory is the death of them, bonobos rapt in their politics and sexual strategizing, phalanxes of eight-year-old murderers in camouflage who'll fire their automatic weapons pointlessly at the swifts, and lowland gorillas, whose hands are likely to end up nailed to the doorpost of a forest hut.

If British swifts have any home other than the sky, this is it: the Congo River Basin, where transpiring trees drag tonnes of wriggling biomass into the air in coughing pulses; where clouds crunch, bellow and unfurl carpets of water; where an oxpecker, plucking a leech from a hippo's eyebrow, flaps and puts up a new crop of minute-old flies with glutinous bodies to fuel the swifts on their way back to English Evensong.

These swifts aren't thinking yet of Evensong, but of eating and soaring. It will be several weeks before they feel a tug and begin to notice, gradually, as a swimmer slowly realises that he's being pulled out by a rip tide, that they are drifting to the north-west, north of where the Congo river spills into the Atlantic.

DRC is a great cultural melting pot for swifts. If you could look up through the forest canopy, ignoring the sunbirds, broadbills, babblers, butterflies the size of dinnerplates, and ice-eyed boomslangs, you'd see hundreds of them fluttering so fast that their wings seem to beat alternately, and then gliding and then vibrating again; all of them black and liquid, like pointed oil drops pouring through the wodge of air above the tree-tops. They all look identically perfect.

Of course they are not identical. The sexes might look the same to us, but they have very different calls, though you might need an oscilloscope to know it. Alongside the experienced birds there are callow first-years, hatched last July, learning natural history (and entomology in particular), geography and flightcraft fast; learning how to deal with a sudden storm-punch to the chin, and what to do if you're stalled by a big lump of salt rain from Brazil, or if the stiff stem of a flight feather bends too much, and how to assemble the neuronal scintillations started by the hair-like microplumes with which the body bristles into a model of its own body in its constantly changing space. And there are two- and three- and four-year-olds, their ovaries and testes starting to redden and swell, wondering, though not in our way of wondering, whether this coming summer will be their time for sex and the scratch of breeze-blocks on their feet, and the frantic gape of nestlings.

These are not the only differences. There are many different populations here: Greek, Turkish, Scandinavian, Swiss, British and so on, separated not by their genetics, physiology or biochemistry, but by their birthplace, their breeding ground, their compass settings and their orientation to the sun and stars.

How do the different groups eye one another as they wheel above the rainforest? Is there an indefinable style of flying that characterises Danish birds, just as the same shirt hangs indescribably differently on Danish shoulders? Do swifts from the Baltic coast have a raffish maritime cosmopolitanism that birds from Basildon, however hard they try, just don't have? Do the swifts hatched in the old Moorish villages clinging to the side of the Sierra Nevada, whose first sight was Africa, just across the strait, have a breezy confidence about migration that makes them swagger round the sky?

Probably there are some of the subspecies *Apus apus pekinensis* that have wintered in Namibia and are bracing themselves now to fly through the Sudan and Egypt, across the Red Sea, Arabia and Iran, brushing the Caspian, and then turning more or less due east through Kazakhstan, north of the Tianshan mountains, through Mongolia, and then winding down into Beijing. Do the other swifts look at them with particular regard, as we revere extreme mountaineers or ultramarathoners?

In one population here in the Congo Basin the testes and ovaries are already ripening and filling, making the abdomen itch and the compass swing. These are the birds of the Near East; of Jordan, Israel, Palestine and what's left of Syria. Swifts aren't doing too well in Syria: they usually like holes in masonry, but not the sort made by artillery shells.

These birds, like those destined for China, will fly through South Sudan, probably hunting the Nile in a focused, restless way (this is a race for nest sites, not a time for sightseeing or fine dining), and over the Red Sea. The Israeli birds surf over the Negev, doing in an hour what it took the Israelites forty years to do, and see Jerusalem gleaming through the haze from 80 miles away.

There's no evidence that swifts change their nationality or religion by marriage or by mere preference. There's no evidence of cross-cultural romance up there above the

Congolese hippos. Of all the creatures on the planet these are the wildest and just about the best travelled, yet they have the cultural and sexual conservatism of the Amish.

Back in the Quirimbas I've given up on the swifts, though I can't suppress the reflex that swivels my eyes skywards.

I've taken to going out at night and lying on my back on the beach, batting off the crabs and rats and feeling every couple of minutes for my wallet, thinking that this view, at least, I can share with the swifts. They're up there somewhere, not worrying much, as they would in the breeding season, about being swept too far by the wind; perhaps sleeping, one half of the brain at a time, like cetaceans.

A First World War pilot, flying at night in a full moon over Vosges, ran into a flock of swifts, black against the white cloud beneath. They seemed motionless. They ignored the plane. His description has a dream-like quality; space and time had both lost their usual significance; the laws of motion were suspended.

To orientate and navigate, swifts probably use the stars, the sun, magnetite particles in their brains or their beaks, rivers, mountains, coastlines, pipelines, field boundaries and, like homing salmon, the scent of home. Since they oscillate between the hemispheres, they must have, at least in outline, a map of the night sky in both hemispheres embedded somewhere in their heads or their bowels. We are truncated animals, and applaud a child who can point out Orion, the Plough and Polaris. We needn't assume that swifts know all 88 constellations (36 predominantly in the northern hemisphere, 52 in the south), but to navigate at night, particularly in the south, they must have a holistic sense of how the heavens are bolted together.

You *can* use the Southern Cross to find south, but it's complicated. You've got to extrapolate an imaginary line down from the vertical poles of the cross, four and a half times the length of the cross, and then drop straight down to the South Pole. It's hard to believe that swifts do that sort of geometry. If they do they're wonderful. And if they don't do it, but nonetheless find south, they're still more wonderful, for they're *feeling* the way that the stars dance together. For that sort of feeling to take you in the right direction you've got to have an absolute chronometer and an absolute calendar – not a calendar driven by your own hormones.

If they're above me now, though, they're not navigating; they're basking in starlight, drunk on it; blinking; half shut-down in the cold, tightly clamped beaks making the grey skin at the corner of the mouth pucker in a stern smile.

I wake at dawn, my face and hands as taut and red as the February ovaries of a four-year-old Israeli swift (but from mosquito bites rather than oestrogen), my boots gnawed by rats, and my wallet presumably halfway to Maputo. And I couldn't care less, because there they are! Six of them. Common swifts, high but unmistakable. Not travelling, not manically stocking up glycogen for the trek north, not even sailing lazily towards Kinshasa; just idling, watching the herds jostle through the bush and the dark shadows of the whale sharks in the channel. They've come back to see me, for what other reason could there possibly be?

Since I'm the big draw, they'll be here, no doubt, for the rest of my time in Mozambique. I'll not betray their trust. I'll use the time well. I'll sketch and paint them badly, and get photos that show the power and the ancientness, and somehow words will come too, though they never have before.

So I'm up and running back to my room and fumbling in my rucksack for my notebook and a box of watercolours and the old heavy camera I usually leave at home, and racing back down to the beach, knocking over a breakfast table as I go, too breathless to apologise.

They're gone. Of course they're gone.

The sky is now dreadful; echoing and taunting. I can't wait to be on the plane and back in Oxford, where at least I can see off the starlings.

I catch a train this morning through freezing drizzle. I fight through the commuters at Liverpool Street station onto an eastbound train, via Colchester, on the sarcastically named 'Sunshine Coast Line'. I get off at Walton-on-the-Naze, on the Essex coast, somewhere between Harwich and Clacton; a prim little place full of painted beach huts and carveries, with its Union Jacks slapping in the wind from Novosibirsk, and step warily between the dog turds and tampons on the bitter beach.

I'm here, of course, because swifts were. Not last August (though they were), but sometime in the early Eocene.

This coast is built on London Clay, which makes the jaundiced yellow-brown brick of much of the capital.

In 1977 a Mr S. Vincent, known to posterity only for sifting through this grudging sediment, found a left humerus, an incomplete right humerus, a left coracoid, an incomplete left ulna and a left radius. They were from a very small bird, crushed into the clay around 56–49 million years ago.

In 1984 C. J. O. Harrison, not of an august academic institution, but of 48 Earl's Crescent, Harrow, HA1 1XN, and possessed of very great erudition, caught the Metropolitan Line to South Kensington, dusted off the bones that S. Vincent had lodged in the Natural History Museum, and noted that the humeri were very short indeed.

They were the humeri of a proto-swift, and S. Vincent was immortal. The bird became *Eocypselus vincenti* ('Cypselus' means 'swifts of the dawn') when Harrison's careful descriptions of the bones were published in a Dutch journal of superb obscurity: 'Tuberculum ventral projects caudally with deep, thin-walled fossa pneumotricipitalis on the distal side', he gravely told the world, 'Deep sulcus ligamentosus traversus below caput curves caudally towards tuberculum ventral. Bicipital intumescentum large…'

S. Vincent's find remained the only *E. vincenti* specimen known until the early second millennium, when other birds were found in the early Eocene Fur Formation in the Limfjord region of Denmark. The relatively well-preserved skull of one of them showed that it was an insectivore. The strikingly short humerus was there, of course, suggesting that the bird was adapted to catching its insects on the wing, but the phalanges of the major wing digits were not as dramatically elongated as they are in modern swifts. The power and virtuosity that make swift-watchers gasp are mostly in the long, feathered fingers. *E. vincenti* was not as breathtaking a flyer as the common swift. And it had much longer toes; it probably perched; it was more tethered to the land.

These new fossils, concluded their major reviewer, meant that the Eocypselids were the 'earliest diverging of the known apodiform [swift] birds.' By around fifty million years ago the swifts were well on the blue whizzing air-road towards *Apus apus.*

Another relative, this time from the Green River Formation in Wyoming. In a deposit there, around 52 million years old, a miraculously preserved swift-like creature was found. It is about 4 ½ inches long and would have weighed less than 30 grammes: it's the smallest bird to emerge from these fecund sediments of an ancient lake. Its wings are intermediate between those of swifts and hummingbirds and so, like *E. vincenti*, it wasn't as aerobatic as modern swifts. It couldn't hover, it ate insects, and astonishingly, we know that it was black. We can see each plume of its feathers, and melanin-containing melanosomes are visible under the microscope. It may well have been iridescent. The fossil is the screen-saver on my laptop. It has displaced the beaming children who should be there.

The Green River swift wasn't the common ancestor of swifts and hummingbirds, but a doomed twig on the family tree. This twig sprouted out into the Eocene, and then withered.

We know, then, that the basic swift blueprint was in place in the early Eocene, and that swifts were refined superbly during the rest of the Eocene (*c.* 33.7–56 million years ago). They fluttered and glided as most of the modern mammal orders appeared. They saw hoofed wolves lumbering down the shore and into the sea to become whales, and saw the hoofs drop off and the tail flukes sprout.

Swifts hatched into an ice-less tropical and subtropical world of high seas and luxuriant forest. The Poles were like Oregon, and London like Indonesia. *E. vincenti* swooped through hot rain between the Essex palms, catching the kind of insects found in Baltic amber. The Green River swifts had to be careful not to be grabbed by crocodiles when they hunted low over the lake.

But the planet was changing. The swifts saw North America and Greenland drifting away from Europe, Australia wrenching free of Antarctica, and India edging north, folding the rock up to form the Himalayas. They felt the crunch and scrape of the sliding plates. And they felt the results: a radical reordering of ocean and sky currents which led to the start of a cooling and drying phase, from 40 million years ago, and the late Eocene extinction of 33 million years ago.

They watched as between 50 and 90 per cent of species in some of the groups they'd grown up with vanished. They saw the seas retreating, trapped in the new ice of the Poles, and they saw the birth of the seasons. They saw the thinning of the great forest stockades, and grasses, later to swarm over much of the earth, emerging on the edges of lakes and rivers. They saw the surviving mammals swell in the new forest glades, and listened as three-toed horses and early hippos, rhinos, camels and pigs neighed, bellowed, wallowed and snorted for the first time.

Swifts don't just surf the green waves of aerial plankton rolling north from Africa. They're not just geographical. They surf time too.

I slap myself out of this reverie on the Walton beach. I'm wet through and my feet are numb. In a chippy in the high street I buy fish of a species already old when the first proto-swifts flew, and catch an over-heated train back to London.

March

In March I was sitting in my room in Palermo. 'Surely it can't be', I said. 'But surely it is.' And so I raced onto the roof, and there they were, spiralling high in the warm air above the cathedral. Swifts: their very first hour in Europe for this year. They weren't there this afternoon; I would never have missed them. They'd ridden the scirocco from Africa and were already prospecting the roofs of Sicily.

I'd waited for them for two weeks, pacing up and down the shore, peering out over the sea, straining for the screams; hoping for dots in the wind from Africa. At dusk I'd climbed a tower to be closer to them if they came in the night. I was frightened that they might come and find no one waiting, and feared what would happen if they did. I got to know the gulls that circled all night round the domes, but they shared the air only with owls and bats. When I was too tired to wait up I sat slumped in my room, reading about winds, tides, feathers and the big things that cranked the world round, until I fell asleep.

For the swifts the sea was a desert. The tall coils of air that fed the swifts on land sometimes keeled over and dumped insects a mile or so out to sea, but mostly the blue-green water was barren. Even the great sand masses of the Sahara were more fertile. Columns of wind, squirming with flies, boinged off mountains and collided over the dunes and the swifts screeched and fed in the spume.

For a moment my eyes flicked away from the birds to my own mind, and to my horror I saw that I'd shifted these swifts to the Straits of Gibraltar. In my head they had just arrived from Morocco, not Tunisia.

I think I know what was going on. The translocation was a symptom of my constitutional inability to inhabit the present moment. But there was more than that. It showed that it's impossible *as a matter of principle* to occupy properly the moment of the swifts' arrival. It's just too big to deal with. The Sicilian swifts blew my fuses, and I had to move mentally a thousand miles west to cool down. And there's something else. The shift was an unconscious recognition of the international heaving-ness of the swifts. Their dashes and flutters make the whole world flash and spin – not just Sicily; not just wherever we happen to be when we see them. Swifts aren't local, and so to think locally about them is bound to misrepresent them. Yes, I know I said that, since we're local creatures, we need to think locally. I stand by it. And it's a problem.

I'm at the back of the plaza of the Western Wall in Jerusalem. It's late morning. I have been here since before dawn. I didn't bring my binoculars. The girl soldiers who search you on the way into the area would think it sinister to use them here. We're at the seam of many worlds.

It smells of cypress, cardamon and tear gas. There is a murmur of prayers and the bustle of earthly busy-ness, but the main sound is the 'wheeeeeee' of swifts.

The Western Wall itself is the retaining wall of what's usually called the Second Temple, built by Herod over two thousand years ago on or near the site of Solomon's Temple, which had been destroyed by the Babylonians in 586 BCE. Jews say that this was the summit of Mount Moriah, where Abraham offered his son Isaac to God. At the heart of Solomon's Temple was the *Kodesh ha Kodeshim*, the Holy of Holies, a sanctuary of desperately dangerous darkness and sanctity, entered only once a year, and then only by the High Priest.

At the heart of the Holy of Holies was the Ark of the Covenant, the gilded wooden chest housing the stone tablets on which the Ten Commandments were inscribed. This was where morality lived.

Moses met God in fire and smoke on the summit of Mount Sinai. The swifts went over it a few days ago on their way from the Congo. Then, extraordinarily, God commanded the Israelites to make a box.

He was very specific about its design and dimensions. It had to have poles so that it could be carried on the shoulders of bearers all the way to the Promised Land – for the law, and God himself, hunched inside the box, were to go with the Israelites. God migrated with them, and the route they took wasn't far off the route the swifts take today.

Two gigantic golden cherubim – high-ranking winged angelic beings – flanked the Ark of the Covenant, bowing their wings over it. God appeared and spoke between the wings of the cherubim: '... there I will meet with thee, and I will commune with thee from above the mercy seat, from between the two cherubims.'

Cherubim were carved into the walls and doors of the

Temple. They may have their origin in Mesopotamia. There they typically have rather square, stubby wings. But in many later depictions of the cherubim they seem to me to have very long terminal phalanges, ideally adapted for prolonged gliding.

The First Temple was levelled, and the Ark of the Covenant went missing, but the sanctity remained, infused into the stones, and filled the new Herodian temple. That too was destroyed, this time by the Romans in 70 CE, but fire and soldiers couldn't touch the holiness. It remains on the Temple Mount, which Muslims believe is where the Prophet landed on his winged horse, Al Buraq, when he arrived on his night journey from Mecca, and from where he made his ascent to the heavens. The Mount is now the site of the Dome of the Rock and the Al Aqsa mosque.

Religious Jews won't go to the Temple Mount, for they might accidentally tread on the site of the *Kodesh ha Kodeshim,* which would be profane and deadly. The sanctity seeps down with the winter rain into the retaining wall, and so the cracks between the stones at the bottom of the wall are crammed with crumpled notes: prayers for healing, a new job, or a marriage, or thanks for the birth of a child or escape from a bomb.

Many of the cracks further up the wall, nearer the source of the holiness, and diving deep into the dark under the Temple Mount, are occupied by common swifts. There are around ninety breeding pairs there – and several hundred more elsewhere in the Temple Mount. No human has touched these nest sites for two thousand years. 'They probably nested here already in the era of King Herod', Amir Balaban, of the Israel Society for Protection of Nature, told an Israeli newspaper.

'… [W]hen the worshippers arrive at sunrise, you can hear

the worshippers' voices from below, and the calls of the swifts from above. It always gives me goosebumps.'

Me too. Rabbi Yosef Cornfeld wrote:

> They start their circling together with the first prayers at sunrise, sometimes circling for several hours in the morning, and then they come back in late afternoon for the afternoon and evening prayers … Usually this behaviour of swifts is called playing, but at least for this flock I think that rather than playing … they are praying …

When they are away in the afternoon they are hunting – over Israel, the Occupied Territories and Jordan. Depending on the wind, they might go up the Jordan Valley, over the Sea of Galilee, catch some of the epic thermals rebounding off the Golan Heights, and hear the thump of the Syrian guns. They might eat nothing all day but aphids from the cedars on the slopes of Mount Lebanon. Every day, whatever the weather, they see the breakers driving ashore at Gaza, Tel Aviv and Haifa.

They distinguish acutely between insect species, but not at all on the basis of national or religious origins. They might come back to the holiest place in the Jewish world with a crop full of beetles caught entirely over the Al Aqsa mosque or the Church of the Holy Sepulchre (the site of the tomb from which, say the Christians, Jesus rose from the dead). They are interested in the checkpoints near Jericho only because there are stands of date palms nearby, and the little flies that feed on the rotting fruit sometimes get drawn up into the sky. The swifts didn't queue for hours in overheated immigration halls to get here from central Africa. Nobody looked at them suspiciously, mocked their style of plumage, or asked them what the hell they were doing. They didn't present their passports meekly, with an ingratiating smile and a fifty-dollar bill tucked discreetly inside.

I think I know what it is like inside one of the swift holes in the Western Wall. I have stayed in the equivalent many times in the Near East: Crusader cellars – low, lightless, arched, with reeds on the floor. And echoing cracks in the side of a wadi looking out onto burning plains of grit or onto the blood-red rock of evening or the thin pink of morning or the curdled blue-that-you-can-spoon of midday.

Though Jerusalem is high in the hills of Judaea, the Western Wall plaza can be a kiln. But inside the Wall, whatever the temperature outside, it is cool in the day and warm at night – like all traditionally built houses in the Levant. From the number of individuals sometimes clustering at the entrance to some of the cracks, it seems that some of the entrances at least are simply the doors of writhing labyrinths, perhaps many feet deep and millennia old, like ancestral badger setts in a hollow hill. The tunnels are built of the bodies of ancient sea creatures – the pale limestone of Judaea which turns gold at twilight. It still smells of lobster – which is a very un-kosher food indeed.

It is dry inside these tunnels; the swifts never build so high up on the Wall that the rain could percolate down to them, and they are so deep inside that a blast of wet wind from the sea off Gaza won't touch them. They are warmer than a swift in the life-draining drizzle of an English May; cooler than a swift under the roasting slates of an English July. 'A day in thy courts', the Psalmist sang to God, 'is better than a thousand.' That's an accurate comparison, from a swift's point of view, of Jerusalem and Oxford.

The swifts' association with the Temple Mount area must go back long before Herod's Temple. When Solomon first built his temple here, mortar wasn't so good and masonry techniques not so refined. That was very good for swifts. The temple, much, much smaller than Herod's though it was, must have had plenty of crevices before it was flattened.

Solomon was proverbially wise. This, says the Jerusalem Talmud, was because he understood the language of birds. The Quran, too, seems to imply that he did, and that it triggered many other blessings: 'Solomon was David's heir', we're reminded, 'and he said: 'O man, we have been taught the speech of all birds, and we have been granted of all things. Surely this is manifest grace.' I like to think that the swifts of the Temple Mount were his teachers. They have certainly opened the heavens and brought grace to many.

Back in Africa there is a great mustering. The Congo whirs. Every day more swifts arrive there from further south. Some are fat from the wetlands of the Okavango, which spawn huge dancing hatches of midges, bouncing up and down in the sun like clouds of chitin yo-yos. Some are fat from the rolling farms of Zimbabwe or the tangled forests of Zambia. And some are thin from the lean pickings of the Kalahari, or from being batted between tropical gales. But there is time enough to catch up; to be ready for the journey north.

Here in the Congo the east and west streams are starting to divide. Some will go north-east, in the wake of the Jerusalem swifts, aiming for the eastern Mediterranean, the Balkans and north-eastern Europe. Others will go west, to the Gulf of Guinea. Amongst the west-bound group are the birds that will find their way to our road in Oxford.

The starlings are snickering and clucking and scrambling in our eaves at the moment. I couldn't evict them. If they're still there when the swifts arrive I'll be tempted to do terrible things.

The end of March is always difficult for me. I feel the swift-seething of the Congo as vertigo. I can't always be in Jerusalem for the foretaste of summer brought by the swifts. It's easier to keep watch in Greece or Sicily, but very nerve-wracking. If they don't come to England, well, I can't blame them. But if they choose not to nest in the southern Peloponnese, or in the amiable villages growing out of the ruddy soil of Marsala, that's bad, significant news.

So I fidget. I prefer to fidget somewhere south, where there's no Wi-Fi to let me switch every few minutes onto the webcam of the Western Wall; where I can watch the sea-sky for those first flecks of quivering black being drawn by their invisible strings out of Africa.

April

They're coming!
They're somewhere out there.

I'm on a cliff-top in southern Spain, on the day's tenth cup of bad coffee, looking south. It's early evening. A band has just started up, and the air is packed with the trembling quarter-tones of North Africa; tunes that in the same cadence tell of loss and triumph. The air is so full of notes that there doesn't seem room for any birds to squeeze in. A wind is pummelling in from the Atlantic, filling my eyes with Moroccan sand.

I've been here every day for a week. My eyes are red with rubbing and watching. I need the coffee to keep me awake. I'm up at first light, worried sick about missing them.

And then, suddenly (it's always sudden) they're here. Just three of them, and at the very edge of vision, which is the only place that you ever see anything really worth seeing. And only for a moment, which is the only worthwhile unit of time. High, silent, fast.

This is a race. Darwin awards the prize.

*

Most of the birds that will breed in western Europe, after milling with all the world's swifts over the Congo Basin, move to Liberia which, after the mid-April rains, sees one of the greatest wildlife gatherings on the planet. It makes the wildebeest migrations in the Maasai Mara and the Serengeti look like a posse of poodles trotting round a suburban park. Beside the Liberian swift-moot, the huge gatherings of hammerhead sharks off Costa Rica and the Galapagos are goldfish swimming meekly round a bowl.

The sky is black with them. How, at those speeds, do they not collide? Hundreds of thousands, gorging on the clouds of insects. Every day, part of the flock buds off and starts the journey, and new swifts from southern and central Africa join the melee. April is the peak time. By the end of April breeders en route to the Netherlands will leave, and they are just about the last of the 'European' birds to go. Some younger birds, not aspiring to breed this season, pause and feed in West Africa a little later, but Liberia is more or less swift-free from early May.

The Liberian fuelling takes an average of a week, but may be as little as four and as many as twelve days. Presumably it depends on how fat they are from Africa; how much weather they've had to flee; whether or not the rains knocked the insects out of the sky. And on how far they have to go. We don't know if the swifts heading to Norway stay longer than those en route to the French Riviera, but it's a fair guess that they do.

I wonder, too, whether the length of stay is partly a question of confidence – and so as variable between individuals as tone of voice is between humans. Do some birds, having been battered by the Bay of Biscay the year before, have to steel themselves to leave, while others, having ridden kind winds in previous years, leave blithely? Whatever the case, the allure of

Liberia is immense. The skies are ambrosial and the weather is warm. Just think, then, how strong must be that northwards tug, tug, tug in the chest.

I wonder if they have a picture in their burnished heads of where they're going? Are memories of our eaves spiralling high above the Gulf of Guinea? Of my face at the window, a few inches away from them as they strike straight up to the nest hole? Of my children in the primary school just down the road, kicking up edible bugs from the field where they play?

They don't seem to prevaricate. One moment they're there, the next they're off, diving straight into the journey. It's the way we should run into cold water.

How do they know where to go? We've no real idea. There's no shortage of speculation.

It's been suggested that blue-light-sensitive flavoproteins in retinal cells act as a compass. When blue light hits these flavoprotein molecules, a pair of highly reactive molecules, each with an unpaired electron, is formed. Those unpaired electrons would make the molecules acutely sensitive to their magnetic environment, and the reaction to that environment (it's suggested) might affect the sensitivity of the photoreceptors, perhaps producing a pattern of dark and light patches in the bird's vision. As the head moves, changing the angle of alignment with the magnetic field, the patches would move. If that's right, the bird has an inbuilt compass, and in some sense it is *looking* at it all the time. When the robin is eyeing your bird table from the tree, it is seeing, too, some kind of visual indication of the location of the North Pole.

A compass is no use unless you know where you're going. You need a map too. Some think that there's a map stored in the beak – created by tiny particles of an iron oxide called magnetite, which can become permanent magnets, and which have been credited with navigational ability in several species. Isn't magnetite, though, just another compass, supplementing the flavoprotein version? Well, perhaps, but it's postulated that magnetite might detect the *strength* of the magnetic field, while the flavoproteins give the direction. Put the two together, perhaps add some memory of landmarks, star-marks or smells (for birds who have made the journey before; it wouldn't help newly fledged birds making the trip to Africa for the first time), and the bird has an integrated navigational system.

It is all very easy to say. It is terribly hard to demonstrate it. I think the most revealing evidence comes from two sources.

The first relates to swifts' adjustment of airspeed in relation to head and tailwinds. The aeronautical engineers' formulae say that a bird aiming to fly most economically should increase its airspeed in head winds and decrease it in tailwinds, and that it makes mathematical sense for a migrating bird to allow itself to drift somewhat with the wind when it is far from its goal, but compensate or overcompensate for that drift when it is nearer the destination.

Swifts migrating at night don't compensate for head and tailwinds, but they do deal with cross winds by adjusting the direction of their flight into the wind to preserve their bearing on the target. Why? It's rather odd. I'd like to believe that it's because swifts are above equations; that they, not the engineers, rule the sky and can re-write the equations with those stubby black beaks if they choose; that they, as god-like birds, can do what they damn well please with Newtonian mechanics.

Others have not rushed quite so fast to mysticism. They have noted, for instance, that nocturnal migration tends to be at high altitude (above 3,000 feet). Might that have something to do with the strange behaviour of the swifts? It's possible. Their compensation for wind drift implies that they are using some sort of visual cues as reference points, and may mean that it is the altitude itself that prevents speed adjustment. That conjecture's supported by observations of swifts migrating by day – for then they *do* adjust their airspeed. The answer may be that adjustment depends on the detection of optical flow – the apparent motion of objects relative to one another. Once you get up really high the resolution of optical flow (dependent on the apparent movement of the land, far below, relative to the swift's own progress) just isn't good enough to allow for it to work at night, whereas it would work in daylight.

The second bit of hard-ish evidence about the possible mechanism comes from observation of other migrating birds. The magnetic field of the Earth is not uniform. There are many anomalies created, for instance, by big iron deposits. Migrating birds, entering these anomalous areas, often drop much closer to the ground. It seems that they have been using a magnetic sense up to that point, but in the anomalous area it has failed, and they have to switch to another system.

Putting these observations together, it seems plausible that the swift transfers its compass bearing (which perhaps tingles in its beak or its eyes) to stars, the moon, a distant rock, or a plume of smoke from factory chimneys, and then uses its eyes as the main instrument of navigation. Or perhaps the rising and falling sun, linked to an internally ticking chronometer, calibrate the bird's own compass, which is then, barring ferrous mountains, used to take the birds to their destination.

I have immersed myself for years in the literature on bird navigation. I am no expert myself, but I have interrogated some of the world's foremost experts on the subject. Every purported answer generates more questions. The more seasoned the expert (as is usual in life), the greater the uncertainty they have.

So it's simple: we just don't know how they do it.

We do know, however, how fast they go and the routes they take. Tiny light-level geolocators on harnesses around their bodies have told us, and tiny GPS systems have been used too.

The whole spring migration, from the moment they swing north to the time they arrive in the Swedish skies (the currently definitive study is on Sweden-breeding swifts) lasts an average of 29 days (with a range of 18–34 days). The average speed is comfortably over 186 miles per day – which takes into account around 27 per cent of the time spent on stopovers. The fastest of the Swedish swifts averaged 403 miles per day.

But that speed is not evenly spread throughout the journey. Up until Liberia, though the migration north has started, the pace is not so brutal. From Liberia, though, it's different. A 'British' swift has been known to do the 3,100 miles from Liberia in about five days – that's 620 miles a day. Sweden-bound swifts in spring have been tracked by radar at about 35 feet per second – which, if maintained for 24 hours, would be 568 miles per day.

It's as if the Gulf of Guinea is the gateway to the stadium. Until they get there they've been sauntering, watching their diet, carbo-loading, limbering up. Over Liberia they're on the starting blocks, steeling themselves for the off.

I'm not so sure that the pause over Liberia is all about food. Yes, there are lots of insects there then, but only after the mid-April rains – and many European swifts will have arrived in Europe by then. They don't seem to load up massively before the big journeys. Five swifts caught soon after arrival at the breeding colony weighed only 0.7 grammes less than they did when they departed on the autumn migration. Admittedly the autumn migration is a more leisurely affair than the spring migration, with more stopovers, and so the imperative for fuelling might not be so great. But even so it is hard to believe that a massive amount of condition has been lost in the entomological flesh pots of central Africa, and that in those days over Liberia they are forcing down everything they can, like foie gras geese. Yes, the journey ahead is arduous, but if a swift can make it to London in five days, is the extraordinary spectacle of Liberia really just about calories? Leaving home is always a painful wrench, however much thermodynamic sense it makes to go. Africa is more home than any other land mass. Perhaps Liberia's a tearful leave-taking.

I find it hard enough to live penned inside a British ring road. What must it be like for the swifts to trade the African sky for three months of slavery to some mewling maws stuck in a hot box? And Africa's a cosmopolitan place for swifts: all the world's swifts are there. In Oxford they'll be with family. Cosy, no doubt, but tense and stifling too.

Another more prosaic factor is doubtless the wind. The swifts starting their northward journey from Liberia in the spring typically get a lot of assistance from tailwinds, as they usually have done further south in Africa too. Awesome though their self-propelled speed and stamina are, they will get to Oxford or Stockholm much faster if they work with the wind; go with the grain of the world.

They are likely to have come with the wind from central Africa to Liberia, climbing high over the dark forest to catch the strong tailwinds of high altitude. From Liberia onwards, until they have crossed the Mediterranean, they'll probably have favourable winds at most altitudes. But it is best for them to be sure.

Over the Gulf of Guinea, in the mornings and the evenings, they climb and climb and climb until they vanish from sight. This *might* have something to do with weather and, especially, wind.

It's now known that they do this throughout the year, and wherever they are – unless they're breeding. These are the twilight ascents, which have probably contributed more to the poetry of swifts than any other element of their behaviour. What are they doing up there, in the thin air?

To understand the debate about this you have to understand that the architecture of the sky is as complex as that of the sea, and that the sky has tides too. It is laminated like a plywood coffee table. A coffee table with tides – tides both along its laminae and up and down across them – and badly clunking similes and clumsily mixed metaphors are necessary to show how woefully all language fails to capture the sky. The tides and the laminae matter very much to the birds swimming through the air, and particularly to those who feed on the insects that swim alongside.

In the day the layer of sky nearest the ground bubbles up as convection currents course through it, producing the turbulence you bump through as your plane comes into land on a sizzling afternoon. And then, overnight, starting at dusk, the sky upends, so that by dawn the rip currents surge parallel to the ground. Over the course of the morning it tilts back up. The sky revolves around two pivot points: dusk and dawn, and if you want to know how it is likely to behave, those are the times to sample it. Going up at those pivotal times also means that you can survey the temperature gradients, which might be relevant in planning where the best hunting is likely to be, and the height gives a better view of distant weather systems.

A thousand feet above the earth you can see clouds full of thunder cruising at an altitude of 6.2 miles that would otherwise be hiding 37 miles under the horizon. By climbing from 3,000 to 6,000 feet, your visual horizon climbs too – from 22 to 99 miles. That might make a difference not only to the menu but to survival.

The quality of the light also changes, just as the wavelengths of light filtering through to the depths of the sea vary with the amount of algae in the water. For at the two twilight pivot points, the polarisation patterns of sunlight are most pronounced, which means that even when the view is clogged with high cloud, the position of the sun can still be seen. If you rely on a compass, as swifts probably do, a twice-daily recalibration of that compass by reference to the sun is vital. The device (whatever it is) for detecting the earth's magnetic field seems to be dependent on light, and to be particularly sensitive to twilight levels.

Work on Alpine swifts has cast doubt on this sampling and surveying hypothesis. They too have twilight ascents, though dawn ascents are twice as common for them as dusk ascents. The ascents are twice as common during their wintering time in Africa than at any other time, including migration. If the ascents were important for orientation, wouldn't you expect them to be *more* common during migration than during the winter? The ascents occur mainly during stable atmospheric conditions. Wouldn't you expect surveying ascents to be particularly important during unstable times? Alpine swifts tend to flap more frenetically at twilight, whether or not they ascend. Since they tend to flap particularly when they are socialising with other birds, might this not imply (some suggest, both for Alpine and common swifts) that the main point of the twilight climbs is *bonding*?

I'm not convinced. Wintering time in Africa is often meteorologically exciting. Those tropical storms can travel fast, shredding everything in their path. There's no such thing as a stable atmosphere in central Africa. And since much of migration takes place at high altitude, there may not be such a need then for calibration every morning and evening: there are already long, high hours when that can be done. But what makes me most doubtful is the fact that, in common swifts, the dawn and dusk ascents take place at exactly the same moment as one another in relation to the sunrise or sunset. Doesn't that suggest strongly that the ascents have something to do with acquiring cues related to the sun?

Whatever the physics of what they are doing, high up there above the Gulf of Guinea, they wait, they climb, they wheel. They taste the wind and watch the clouds. They feel the swellings in their pelvis. With a sudden spurt of resolve they're off.

The best route isn't the shortest. The route the Swedish-breeding swifts take is about 43 per cent longer than the straight line. From Liberia in the spring they do the journey so fast that feeding en route probably isn't a major issue – though up to then it had been. No: these spring detours are mainly about catching the best winds.

They cut across the Gulf of Guinea itself, in the wake of thousands of previous generations, looking down on the tankers and container ships boring through the swell, on the breakers coming into land in Sierra Leone, Guinea, Guinea-Bissau, Senegal, the Gambia and Mauritania – breakers that may have been started by the bows of the ship that carried that slave-trader from Lisbon to Mozambique, and might have been ricocheting to and fro across the Atlantic like billiard balls ever since. Sometimes they're inland, bumping down into the holes left when the brown land pulls the air down into itself, and thrust up by the pulsing thermal mushrooms sprouting from the forests.

'What's it like?' I ask my friend Mark, an Airbus test pilot who has flown the swifts' route many times.

'The first part of the journey from West Africa is terrifying', he says. 'Vast convective currents boil up from the jungle.' In the mornings the forest starts to fizz: energy is pumped into the atmosphere from below, and storms build. 'They're deadly', said Mark. 'We avoid them by using forecasts, satellite imagery, and radar.'

But what about the swifts? The electric sky makes the tiny filoplumes on the end of their feathers stiffen and buzz. From many miles off they hear the mumble of the flat-topped cumulonimbus thunderheads, and scatter before they're slapped and ground into the forest canopy.

The desert is different, says Mark. The updrafts and downdrafts are still there, but they're less scary than over the forest, and if you climb (as the swifts often do in this phase of the migration), the air smooths out. Visibility is often poor at lower altitudes – fogged by suspended dust and sand – but up high, and particularly at night, it is often magnificent. The air is cooled from the chill land below, convection slows, and the sky is left again to its regular currents.

For most of us at night, it is light down here, and we look up into a dark sky. But in the Saharan sky at night it's the other way round: dark below, broken by the light from occasional settlements and the winking pinpricks of light from nomads' fires, but effervescent light above, splashed over the whole dome of the visible universe. The Earth has ceased to be. There's nothing below those strange-toed swift feet, now tucked into their bodies for warmth. The reality is *up*.

'After many dusty and oppressive miles', says Mark, 'the Mediterranean appears as a delight. As you approach from the south, it's hidden for a long time by the Atlas mountains, and then it's suddenly there, a glistening band of blue and gold in the day; a fringe of neon in the night.' The winds are suddenly more difficult too. There's often a northerly wind, straight in the face, with cumulus clouds to skirt or dive through. From now on the journey is likely to be more difficult.

We tend to think of the Mediterranean as a merry, benign, controllable, recreational sea. Sailors know otherwise. There is a reason that Poseidon the Earthshaker, whose court is under the Mediterranean, is never shown smiling. His caprice is as notorious as his arm is strong.

This is what he chose to do one year, in early April.

Suburban gardens in Athens were filled with shivering, battered flycatchers. Throughout southern and central Greece tens of thousands of swallows and martins huddled together on roofs, balconies and roads, too cold and too tired to move. There were thousands of swifts too, crammed into ventilation ducts and rammed under tiles. Clusters of them swung from wires like swarms of bees, the first one hanging upside down like a bat, the others clinging on, digging their nails into their neighbours' wet feathers.

They'd all hit an icy, vicious northerly wind over the Cyclades, and were forced to land on the eastern coast of mainland Greece. Most of them were doomed. The Balkans and eastern Europe were quieter that summer.

I can understand Poseidon hating Odysseus, but swifts, swallows and martins? Perhaps if they weren't all such masters of the air he wouldn't have felt that he had to punish their hubris.

I stay for a while in Spain; still looking up and out over the sea. The three swifts were followed the next day by another trickle, and then the trickle became a gush, and the gush became a flood. Now it's time to head back to Oxford to unroll the red carpet.

I book a window seat on the plane, as I always do, so that I can see what *they* will see. But it just reminds me how much more alive they are. I sit hunched in a metal tube full of farts, thrumming towards Heathrow. If the plane turned round and went due south I'd be in Timbuctoo before I began to suspect we were going the wrong way. If I walked home from Gibraltar people would think I was a Homeric hero or a maniac.

When I get off the plane, I'm embarrassed to think that *they* will be arriving soon. I want to tidy the place up for them – but that would mean demolishing England. On the bus down the M40 I'm squirming. I wouldn't want to eat bugs born on that roadside. Can't we offer them anything better? It would be a great personal sacrifice for me, but can't I somehow tell them that they'd be better off in Norway, or the Peloponnese, or even, if they must come here, in Snowdonia or the West Highlands?

'Don't come: please don't come', I pray – not under my breath either, from the looks I get. And I wonder at the same time what will happen to me if they don't.

Sometime between the end of April and May 10 the Dutch swifts leave West Africa. Africa won't have any common swifts now until June, when the Israeli swifts begin to arrive back.

May

My prayer is answered. They're not coming. My toes can uncurl.

Friends email me jubilantly from all over Europe. 'They're here!' 'Ils sont arrivés!'

'Έχουν φτάσει!' 'Ellos han llegado!' 'Sono arrivati!' 'Eles chegaram!' 'Vardilar!' 'Sie sind angekommen!' 'Iritsi dira!' 'Han arribbat!' 'Dorazli!' Always with an exclamation mark, because words fail. Always in their own language first, before they switch to English to give me the details, as if they want to claim the swifts in the language the birds will be hearing for the next three months: to assert that the birds really are there, that they're Czech birds for a while, or Catalan or Greek.

The rest of the message is always the same: gratitude (though it's rarely clear to whom) and relief; the exact time of arrival; the numbers of birds; reports from elsewhere in the country; high hopes for nestlings; worries about the weather forecast and what that might mean for the insect harvest; and, from the swift professionals, a spot of self-congratulation. Their recordings of swift screams are already broadcasting loudly from the amplifier in the upstairs bedroom, hoping to lure the birds to the deluxe nestboxes, installed in March at great risk to life and limb.

But here, nothing. Reassuringly silent skies. I won't have to apologise to them; to shift embarassedly from foot to foot when they're feeding, knowing that the food's far better in the Taygetus mountains. I won't need to look shamefacedly up when they're screaming down between the terraced houses, knowing that it would be far better to scream around a village somewhere above Lucca.

I'll cope. I'll go to see them in the Peloponnese and Tuscany, and they'll see me too and might give me some credit for the most excellent flies they'll find there, and for the warm tunnels in the mediaeval walls, rather than resenting me for living in this place, not far from the edge of the swift-world, where it's cold and dank and smells stale. And, best of all, I'll be spared the desolation of their departure: the hollowness and panic that comes when you wake and know that there's something wrong, and then realise with a jolt what it is – that there's no 'wheeeeeeeeeeeee' from outside.

It's going to be a great summer. I'll have swifts, but when and where I want them, and on my terms. If we lived in Iceland I could have this every summer. Perhaps we'll move there.

I'm sitting in the kitchen a couple of days later, reading *Njal's Saga*, when there's a rumpus upstairs, and Jonny, our nine-year-old, runs down, screeching. I can't make out what he's saying at first. Probably another front has opened in the civil war with his sister. But now he's down here, out of breath, panting: 'They're…'

'What, Jonny?'

'They're… '

'Who? What?'

'They're…… here!'

He grabs my hand and drags me outside. Yes, there *they* are, high, high, high, but unmistakable because swifts are more themselves than anything on or above the Earth.

Perhaps Liberia served up an irresistible glut of ballooning spiders just as they were about to leave. Perhaps they banked on a Saharan tailwind that didn't come. Perhaps they climbed too high on the air spouts of the Atlas, looked back at Africa, and had second thoughts about the whole strategy of migration. Perhaps they hit a squall off Gibraltar, dawdled in the deep cool valleys of the Pyrenees, laboured through driving rain in Biscay, or looked long and enviously at the gable end of a farm in north Devon.

But they came here because, ludicrously, they regarded this drab street in some limited sense as home. They began life here, and beginnings determine the whole course of things, and their beginnings doomed all their dynasties to see this as home; to pass up a crack over a spicy souk in Anatolia, a marble cave under a Corinthian lintel in Sicily, an abandoned castle on a cliff-top in Transylvania, and a grotto in a mediaeval villa outside Naples, where they could have made a nest from the pages of a seventeenth-century Bible that's rotting in a barn. It is madness to be squashed inside the Oxford bypass instead. It is insane to opt for a nest of shitty pigeon feathers snatched from the updraft of the Tesco air-con.

Indeed the whole liaison with humans, shrewd once, doesn't look so smart now. Before humans built houses, which wasn't so long ago, common swifts must have nested, as they still very occasionally do, in crevices in cliffs and holes in trees. But then they threw in their lot with us.

One of the earliest pieces of evidence of human habitation in England is at Boxgrove in Sussex. The settlement there is around half a million years old. It was littered with the rather basic stone tools of that era and with animal bones. Among the bones were the bones of swifts. That doesn't mean that swifts nested in the human dwellings as they nest in our house, but it might mean that they lived at quite close quarters, perhaps (it is suggested) nesting in the nearby cliffs and foraging over the water. There's good reason to suppose that humans and swifts cohabited in late Glacial Surrey, in Tuscany around 700 BCE, in Roman Winterbourne, mediaeval Oxfordshire and Canterbury Cathedral.

For a while swifts and humans did splendidly together. Tree-hole dwellers suffered as the forests were fired to make room for crops, dwellings and domestic animals, and felled for houses and ships, but the number of anthropogenic holes massively increased, and swift numbers with them.

But marriage is dangerous, and the marriage of swifts and humans is on the rocks. The RSPB and BTO estimate that UK swift numbers fell by 41 per cent between 2008 and 2018. In China, swift numbers have declined by around 60 per cent since the mid-1980s.

There are no doubt many reasons. We have chemical, antiseptic, monocultural farming practices that discourage insects. We've poisoned many of the remaining insects, and the feisty survivors of the poison bear toxic residues that build up in the bodies of anything that eats them. Climate disruption means that swifts can't rely on warm, dryish European summers to serve up to the fledglings the biomass they need to get into the air. The weather throughout the year, and, importantly, on the migration routes, is volatile and often angry. But probably even more deadly than these challenges (which of course affect many species) is our pathological tidiness. We just don't like holes in our houses or office buildings. That affects swifts very particularly.

In the Neolithic we started carving up the world. We built walls across it to separate things that had once been part of a whole. Behind some of the walls we penned the animals we had previously seen as our ensouled cousins, and behind some of the walls we penned ourselves. In some of these Neolithic walls – which were really symptoms of a disastrous mania for control that has dominated and blighted us ever since – lived common swifts. If you choose to make your home in the manifestation of a disease, it's probably not going to go well with you in the long term.

'Do you still want to live in Iceland, Daddy?' asks Jonny. He's been worrying.

'Of course I don't,' I reply, but to be honest I'm not sure. I'm a very, very Neolithic man, and I'm disconcerted when something in the wild world won't be contained; when anything in the world is really wild; when it won't arrive and leave on cue – my cue. And I don't deal well with the sickening annual rollercoaster: Will they? Won't they? When? Where? I can't train myself not to care, and this, like all vulnerabilities, is painful and exhausting. If I didn't know that not to be vulnerable is invariably fatal, I probably would move to Iceland. Or Argentina. Or New Zealand. Anywhere without common swifts.

*

They're here, and I have to make the best of it. I have to cope with my exaltation, and the flames of a passion that looks perverted, and the slow burn of a dread of loss that consumes a bit more of me every summer day. For the moment the earth works, more or less in the old way, and I have to rally and reinvigorate my old and failed ways of trying to understand this working.

'Get over yourself', urges a brisk and prosaic neighbour. 'Get a life. Some birds come from Africa, right. They're nice birds. We like watching them. They eat, they fuck, they feed their babes, they go, they come back, and then they do it all over again. End of story.'

Yes, yes, end of story, I suppose. If there ever is an end to any story. Which there isn't.

The very first time they flew into my life was on this day in May when I was eight. I was sitting in a field in Yorkshire counting the house martins so that I could put the number in my nature diary for the day – for I was a Neolithic child as I am a Neolithic adult: a mapper, a categoriser, a constrainer. I thought that to measure was to understand.

Then, just above the martins, there was something else. These, I thought, were cut from a different cloth (I'd just learnt the expression from a nineteenth-century book of piratical derring-do). They seemed to be made of gunmetal, not feathers and flesh. The words that came to hand as I groped to tell myself what I was seeing were the martial words that stud so many of the swift poems. These swifts sliced, slashed, bore down and executed.

Their poise was terrifying. Nothing, surely, could ruffle

them, let alone kill them. I could see the martins deferring to the air; doing what it suggested. I could see their wings tremble with the effort of turning, and their breast feathers ripple. But the swifts controlled the sky, absolutely, peerlessly and, for that little boy, agog in the field, intoxicatingly.

This might well have turned out badly. Courtesy of the swifts, I might have become fixated on guns and power. Swifts might have turned me into a Fascist. No one should be allowed to watch swifts until they've had a rigorous historical and political education.

I escaped from Fascism later that summer. My hobby was taxidermy. I spent my pocket money on glass eyes and formalin, and I had a fast-growing collection of badly stuffed specimens and pickled things in jam-jars. When the doorbell rang it was likely to be a child with a corpse, as it was that July.

This corpse, in a paper bag from Fletchers the Sheffield baker, was a newly fledged swift. It must have tipped prematurely out of the nest and, scuffling helplessly along the ground, been taken by a cat. There were puncture wounds in its abdomen, and gut contents dribbled out. Its eyes were open and dry. Its wings were still scythes, but now they would cut nothing except the air of my bedroom when I suspended it on a thread over my bed. Its feet were odd and the claws sharp, and I hoped the cat hadn't got off scot free. Its short black beak, which in six weeks' time should have been snapping at the flies bred in the dung of Congolese forest elephants, was helplessly open, as if to get a last gasp of the air that was its home or (I later thought) to let out its soul.

There was no mastery here. I didn't think: how are the mighty fallen. I thought instead that there are no mighty, which was a better conclusion. Vulnerability, I decided, was part of the web and weave of the universe. It was a dead fox, a few years later, that made me realise that death is inevitable (if something as alive as a fox can die, how can *anything* escape?), but that young swift paved the way for terror.

I don't play the recorded swift sounds on the MP3 player. Our hole is taken. Swifts have lodged there for the last seven years or so. A fastidious friend, who would dearly love to have swifts in her house, won't use the recordings either. 'I want them to choose me of their own free will, or not at all. I don't want to engineer them in any way. They're valuable precisely because they've got nothing to do with me. If they ignore me and my lovely roof, that's fine.'

I know what she means, but it's misguided. All the recordings do is draw the swifts closer so that they get a look at some nest sites that they might otherwise have missed. Despite appearances, and despite our intuitions, they are neither omniscient nor omnipresent. They are not gods, or if they are, gods can be broken and compromised.

Henry Williamson, lying on one of the joists in his attic in Devon, watched a starling pulling out one of the crucial flight feathers of a swift. 'The terrified bird scrambled down to the light under the eave. It attempted to fly, but whirled down to the street, where it could only crawl helplessly. Meanwhile the starling threw two white eggs after her, then settled to lay the first of five azurine eggs in the nest.'

We failed to plug our eaves against the starlings, and they bred there, but they bred early and didn't try for a second clutch. Our eaves should be clear.

★

Swifts arrive here in what the German swift biologist Ulrich Tigges describes as the Advance Guard, the Vanguard, the Main Body and the Rearguard.

There are very few birds in the Advance Guard – typically one or two, or sometimes small flocks of up to five birds are seen in an area. Having shown themselves, and generated a typhoon of ecstatic emails and tweets, they often disappear completely for days. Goodness knows what they're doing or where they go when they vanish. Are they ambitious would-be first-time breeders without an established nest site, who have a memory from their scouting trips the previous summer of where they might find a site, and who have raced here from Africa to claim it? If so, do they hope to displace the birds that nested there the previous year? Will they wait in or around the hole, to greet the established occupants with claws and hissing? Or are they remembering an unoccupied hole from last year? Or do they remember that a previous occupant was taken by a hawk in Zambia, or swallowed by a cyclone in Malawi?

We have no idea – though perhaps the fact that they are seen in one area for a short time, and then disappear, might mean that they are prospecting for nest sites outside the area of the colony where they themselves hatched. Until we have much more accurate tracking data we won't begin to be able to attempt an answer. Perhaps they just do it to tease.

The Advance Guard are joined after ten or eleven days by the Vanguard – the first arrival of the breeders, thinks Tigges. They seem to know what they're about. They go confidently and proprietorially to holes, and begin their business.

Who are the Vanguard? Again, we don't know (this is the thrilling, ever-repeated mantra in any conversation about swifts). Perhaps they are strong, experienced birds; fast-flyers and confident navigators; happy to cross the Sahara and the Mediterranean by themselves or in small groups; birds who don't feel the pull of Africa so much, for they know they'll be back there soon; birds who know that the sooner they knuckle down to the hard graft of breeding, the sooner it will be done. Or perhaps it's about status in the colony (although what advantage high status confers or low status denies in already-paired birds who already have a designated nesting site nobody knows) and early arrivers have pole position in the race for status. Or perhaps they are anxious, ambitious would-be breeders, or birds who missed out on a nesting site because of a late arrival last year and don't want to make the same mistake again this time.

The Main Body arrives around three days after the Vanguard, and from now, in a swift area, all other species seem to evaporate. I don't notice anything in the air from mid-May until early August.

Who are the Main Body? You know the answer now: we don't know. Are they high-ranking, establishment figures, so self-assured that they needn't hurry to Oxford because they know that no one would dare to take their nest hole? Or are they naive, querulous birds, feeling the need for company on the long voyage, willing to risk homelessness and a year of barreness for the security of a crowd?

And the Rear Guard? They come several weeks after the main body. They are immatures, probably without the aspiration, and certainly without the expectation, of breeding this year. Many will have hatched just the previous year, and will not have made the journey north before. Other non-breeders will be more experienced (swifts may well not breed until their third or fouth year). The non-breeders come to learn the reproductive ropes and the map; to prospect for nest sites that might be serious options in subsequent years; and to talk and bond with the others.

These four distinct parties denote a clearly stratified swift society. Though we can see some of the more obvious strata, we do not know the rules for moving between them. Though the swift colony in the Oxford University Museum of Natural History is one of the longest continuously studied colonies of any bird in the world (David Lack started his observations there in 1948), and there is an immense amount of data, every new graph deepens and compounds the mystery.

Swifts are colonial, highly social birds. A colony might be anything from three to thirty-four pairs, and loyalty to the colony is an important, though negotiable, part of swift life. Once a nesting hole is established, the same pair are likely to return to it year after year, for swifts, like many long-lived birds, are monogamous. Genetic studies showed that in a high-density colony only 4.5 per cent of chicks were the result of extramarital affairs.

In the zoological world the tendency to monogamy is generally correlated with relative brain weight – and hence with cognitive ability. Promiscuous animals, by and large, have smaller brains, for *relationship* demands a good deal of neurological processing power, and promiscuity is a denial of relationship. Monogamy, as many of us know, is costly and hard: it demands work, though the pay-off can be profound. The work is often *emotional* work: give and take; forgiveness and forbearance.

For the last decade or so it has not been so embarrassing to talk about animal emotion – and it should not have been ever since Darwin's epic (though almost unread) *The Expression of the Emotions in Man and Animals* (1872). Are swifts emotional? Probably. Do their emotions relate in any way to ours? Probably. Do their emotions, if any, map neatly onto ours? Certainly not. But anthropomorphism, as the American biologist Carl Safina puts it, is a good first guess as to what an animal is feeling. I share most of my evolutionary history, my neurological software, and my physiological hardware with swifts. It would be very surprising if, when a swift nestling plunges from the nest site and is dashed on the pavement below, a swift feels nothing at all akin to what I'd feel at the death of a child. Nothing like as intense, I've no doubt. Not remotely as crippling, I'm sure (I'd never recover), but perhaps something of the same sort of desolation.

It seems likely that the non-breeders will hope (do they *hope?* How can they not? Is there really a more scientific word?) to breed in the colony in which they were hatched, and into which, until they come to try to breed themselves, they have poured so much energy and attention. Three years circling the colony, of feeding with its members, of looking longingly at holes, and this year, wondering if X, who looked weak and bedraggled in Ghana, might not have made it across the Sahara after all, creating an opportunity.

The colony means the ability to know, intimately, a few individuals. It is a school for the art of relationship, and no doubt of the rules of hierarchy too. It means knowledge of a *type* of space different from all other space in a swift's life. They are intercontinenal animals; they fly to where the air is thin; their perspective is often that of a small-scale map, if not a satellite. But in the colony they learn that life is really all about a few square fusty inches of real estate; that that's what the typhoon-dodging and the rhino-buzzing and the twilight flights over the Mountains of the Moon are *for*.

Colonies seem to have territories, often bounded (thinks Tigges) by man-made features: a big road, or a rank of office buildings, or a shopping mall, with zones of no-man's land separating them from the territories of neighbouring colonies. One colony Tigges studied in Tel Aviv, for instance, has an area of nearly 110,000 square yards. If a swift were asked 'Where are you from?' it would give the coordinates of the territory, and would-be breeders probably search for nest sites first within that area. But it's increasingly hard to get on the property ladder, and they may be forced to look elsewhere. That won't be easy. Imagine an impoverished young Croatian turning up in South Uist, going into the pub, and saying that tomorrow he's going to marry a local girl and take up farming. It's like that.

Swift territories probably help to defuse tension and reduce dangerous violence between swifts. Those strange clawed feet can kill. The territories have, then, precisely the opposite effect to that of human nations. If a swift knows that the three corners of its patch are, clearly, the Stock Exchange, the HSBC building and the mega-roundabout, it'll be likely to be content with its lot, to restrict its house-hunting to that area, and so avoid confrontation with other communities. Possession, for swifts, doesn't create an expansionist appetite for more possession. Having a place should make us more secure, not less.

How those bounds are originally set is unclear, and we know nothing at all about the policing of the frontiers other than to note that during the breeding season there doesn't seem to be much active patrolling. It's unecessary. The frontiers seem to be quietly respected during the breeding season.

This might be a rosy-tinted view of territoriality. It may be that the Vanguard, for instance, are border police, dispatched early to check that the barbed wire fences have survived the winter, that the minefields are intact, and that no one is where they shouldn't be.

Whatever the territories and the four waves of arrival mean, they mean that the swift world is like ours, class-conscious and constrained by rules in addition to the Laws of Motion. There are politics, conventions and statutes up there in the blue. But they're not really like us: sociopathy, vanity and talentlessness are emphatic disqualifications for leadership, rather than, as for us, essential elements of the CV.

As soon as the breeders return they occupy the nest sites. If they don't, someone else will, and the summer is short. Two days after Jonny dragged me outside, I hear the scratching above my study which means that it's going to be all right for another year, and see the birds dart up, as straight as a plumbline, to the angle of the eaves. My face is a few feet from them.

I've never seen the nest. But I know what's in there. I've looked into the nestboxes in the Oxford Natural History Museum, and I'm addicted to a swift nestbox webcam in Belgium.

The nest will be a casual, sluttish assembly of anything that can be snatched from the air: grass strands, lottery tickets, broken butterflies, dandelion seeds and newspaper headlines finally put to good use. Swifts don't weave: there's no time for artistry – and no need. Usually the eggs can't roll far. The junk pile is stuck approximately together with strands of saliva.

The parents are unlikely to arrive together. They may well

not have seen one another since they left here for Africa last August. More than three quarters of pairs arrive in and leave Oxford at different times, but seeing the other again has been the reason for flying across the planet. They have, quite literally, been living to see one another. It is pointless to try to imagine how the reunion feels. You really would be able to shout 'Anthropomorphic!' then.

Swifts have interesting sperm – very different from the sperm of perching birds. The microtubules in the spermatid (the haploid male gamete, containing half of the genetic information necessary to form a zygote) form a single row encircling the cell. And these sperm travel down from the abdominal testes to the male's cloaca, waiting there for an opportunity.

That opportunity is likely to come either in the sweaty dark of the nestbox, around seven o'clock in the morning or six o'clock in the evening, or in the sky. In the sky it is quick and easily missed. Probably those 4.5 per cent of extramarital chicks began their lives in the sky when the female lifted her wings into a 'V' to show that she was ready, the pair spread and tilted their tails so that, for the crucial moment, they were travelling at the same speed, and the male rested on her back. His tail went up, hers went down, and he pressed his full cloaca against her empty one. For a moment, with two pairs of parallel wings spread, they looked like a tiny bi-plane.

Much is said about swifts mating in the air, but it's probably unusual, and it has a furtive air about it.

About a fortnight after the arrival of the second partner, assuming reasonable weather, white eggs are squeezed out into the spit-glued mess, generally some time in the morning. Throughout the whole of that morning the hen stays in the nest: it's a sort of labour, after all. If the weather's bad, laying is delayed until the fifth day after it improves – if it does. Does the hen, soaring around with her quiescent embryos inside her, formulate a weather forecast and herself decide that the egg-production switch should be flicked? Or is there, perhaps embedded in her brain-stem, some sort of meteorological thermostat, triggered by temperature or merry summeriness?

Before the parents settle down to the arduous business of incubation and child-rearing, at least some of them are away from the box at night – presumably climbing into the atmosphere to socialise and sleep. It's as if they're relishing their last bit of freedom before the grind of breast-feeding and the school run. As in the human suburbs, so in the swifts' sky. 'Some individuals have been much more prone to do this than others', wrote David Lack.

There's a whole library of books to be written about the individuation of animals. They're not identical automata. 'The Animal Will', the lead title should be called, and swifts should be the cornerstone. Their preferences and foibles are more eloquent than those of dogs, cats, horses or any other domestic animal, simply because it's impossible to know where a dog or a horse ends and its owner begins: we've co-evolved with them so long and so intensely that the biography of a horse or dog is in part an elliptical biography of the owner. But swifts are owned by no one: in their options you see unfettered wild choice.

*

The eggs (usually two or three, but sometimes, and counterproductively, four) are robust – very resistant to cold and parental neglect – and incubation won't usually begin until they're all out. From now on the parents are tied. Both the cock and the hen incubate. They take it in turns: one incubates (for up to six hours at a time) while the other collects food.

After twenty or so days, the first egg hatches. Twenty-four hours later, the second egg follows, and twenty-four hours after that, the third. If there's a fourth egg, it will hatch another twenty-four hours after the third, but it needn't bother: all fourth nestlings will die.

If it's cold, hatching will take longer. The parents, instead of brooding diligently, will have carefully considered the lifetime breeding success statistics filed in their subconscious, and flown off in the late morning and throughout the afternoon to feed themselves, leaving the eggs cold and alone. Probably the eggs will be fine: they're very resistant to the cold, and embryonic development is effectively arrested until the sun and the parents return.

It makes sense for the parents to look after themselves. The commitment now is nothing to what it will soon be. When the eggs hatch there will be little rest. There's no point in the parents draining themselves dry now. In fact there's no point in the parents draining themselves dry at all. Nervous fledglings would do well not to know evolution's calculations. Though there is a huge investment in the young, it is not investment to the point of death. It's one thing working hard to give your children opportunities you never had; it's quite another to give yourself a heart attack doing it. In birds as long-lived as swifts, and with such high annual survival rates, overall lifetime reproductive success is best achieved by living to breed another year – even if that means sacrificing the brood or part of it.

I have a picture of what's going on in our eaves.

The entrance to the eaves is a small crack which can only be reached by flying straight up. Then there's a squeeze, but the squeeze is a good thing: it means that nestlings are less likely to topple out when they start wandering.

There are no nestlings yet, just a small black bird squatting on a pile of rubbish about 18 inches from the tunnel mouth. Swifts don't seem to have good vision in low light, and they can't see much more than I could: just the outline of the sitting bird and, importantly, the white throat patch. If the bird (it could be a male or a female) shifted, I'd see two eggs, plain white, like the eggs of most birds who nest in Stygian places.

Beneath and behind are rafters, lined haphazardly with sharp pink fibreglass. Generations have picked at it, thinking that it might be good for the nest, but the fibres pricked them, and they left the strands hanging. Above are the naked roof tiles. It can be an oven. It can be a fridge. There's a broken tile further on, which we've been meaning to get fixed for ages. When it rains, water drips onto the rafters and rots them, and the place smells of mould.

In my mind's eye their space under our eaves is covered with graphs, pie-charts and long lists of targets, reminding the swifts what they've got to do and when, or else.

I wonder what they think of us. Do they hear, as I do, the fingers-down-the-blackboard dissonance between the elegance of their ethereal lives and the clumpiness of mine?

I wonder where the frontiers of this colony are, and whether the birds have possessive thoughts as our children do: 'mine', 'not yours'. I wonder if the nestlings, when they're hatched, will look out at the patch of light at the end of the nest site and say: 'That's where life *really* is.' They must have some sort of aspiration, and it must be fiery and fierce. Is it coded in any way like ours?

'They're *birds*, for Christ's sake!' an ex-friend helpfully reminds me, trying to bring me back down to earth. But it's no good: the swifts aren't down to earth at all.

5th May swift roosting 10.37pm 15℃

6th May 8.30am swift about to leave nest box

June

June, for the nestlings, is the make-or-break month. If the weather is warm, it will be a good swift year in Britain. In these unforgiving islands, overall breeding success correlates with average June temperatures. In kinder places, there is no such correlation. Umbrian swifts need not look nervously at the thermometer: there's much more slack in their system. Above a certain temperature threshold – routinely reached in clement southern places, insect numbers aren't significantly related to temperature: below that threshold, they are.

'A young swift, like a young songbird, is hideous', wrote David Lack. They are naked feeding and growing machines. Their guts are so big for their weight (15 per cent of body weight, compared to 10 per cent in a newly hatched quail, which is of comparable weight) that they push the cloaca onto the nestling's back. It retreats to the conventional position by the time the bird takes to the air. Young swift brains, on the other hand, are, as a percentage of body weight, about half the size of a young game bird's. They really don't have to think much for the first few weeks.

Sometimes naked nestlings fall to the ground and are killed. If you find one, pick it up and look closely. Its skin will be like pale-pink tissue paper, and you'll be able to see its liver, like a big bruise, and the gut, full of insects drowned in their own juice.

It looks so weak, and indeed swift nestlings can do little for a while other than open their mouths for food, jostle their siblings when another cropful of air-plankton arrives, and defecate skywards through their eccentric cloacas. But in fact they are tremendously tough. In an average of 43 days (with a weather-dependent range of 37–56 days), they will be ready to fly to Africa. Until then, they face a number of challenges. The most important are an irregular food supply, the related problem of cold, life-threatening competition from their siblings, the one-chance launch into the air, and vampires. We'll come back to the first flight when its time comes, and look for a moment at the other threats.

The nestlings' food comes from the air, via the parents, and, as we've seen, the insect mass in the air is, up to a point, dependent on the temperature. The sort of wet, cold, miserable June that most Britons think is typical can be deadly. Rations are short, and the parents have to feed themselves first.

Evolution knows exactly how wretched British summers can be, and has designed the physiology of young swifts accordingly. They can be left unbrooded for many hours, and sometimes days, as both parents comb the capricious winds.

The nestlings go into a sort of quiescence: a partial hibernation. Their body temperature falls and their various organ systems switch to the lowest level of metabolic activity consistent with survival. They look moribund, but a few minutes of brooding and a few mouthfuls of insects will revive them completely, as though nothing had happened. They might take a little longer to leave the nest, but otherwise seem to be none the worse. Songbird nestlings would be dead in a few hours if they were left. Their food comes from near to the nest, and the supply is less erratic than that of swifts, and so they haven't had to invest presumably expensive resources in a survival system like the swift's. If a clutch of baby blackbirds isn't brooded and fed for three hours, it's because its parents are dead, and if that's so, no amount of metabolic cunningness will save them. Long-absent swift parents, on the other hand, might have decided to go hunting in Amsterdam, and it might well be worthwhile for the nestlings to hang on for as long as they can.

The tight energy budget and the unpredictability of the supply chain mean that a swift's worst enemies, apart from the British weather, are its siblings. The nest is the unregulated market. No quarter is given. Nature is as red in beak and claw in the comfort of the swift family home as it ever is between prey and predator in the Serengeti, or between Rachel and Jonny over Haribos.

Overall, around 19 per cent of nestlings die, and nestling mortality increases with hatching order – to 100 per cent for fourth-hatchers. David Lack thought that sequential hatching was a mechanism to facilitate the selective starvation of the youngest chick during lean times: there has been less investment in that chick, so less is wasted, and it is also more obvious which victim must be sacrificed to save the other chicks and the parents. It's the smaller, younger, weedier one.

Only rarely, though, is the weather so dreadful that a choice this stark has to be made. Usually a miserable June or July will just mean an extended time to fledging and departure. Sometimes, though, the summer fails dramatically. Then some stern algorithms cut in.

The parents won't sell themselves short for the sake of the children. They know that their *lifetime* breeding success will be higher if they look after themselves in June and July, and if that means starving the nestlings, the nestlings will starve. That makes sense, not only because of the lifetime breeding statistics, but also because parents who die or are too weak to forage in June or July aren't any use to the insatiable offspring. Parental self-interest is, again up to a point, the interest of the young.

I can't help wondering what it *feels* like to be ruled by these despotic algorithms. The parenting instinct is immensely strong. It spurs the birds to colossal journeys and Herculean food-gathering efforts. And yet there sometimes comes a time when, seen with the perspective of a swift's long life expectancy, it no longer makes sense to be a parent that summer; no longer makes sense to try to preserve the massive reproductive investment of that year. The arithmetic would be completely different if swifts didn't live so long. If, like most birds their size, they were ephemeral things, likely to be dust in a year or two, it would make sense to sacrifice themselves on the altar of their children's future, and they would meekly accept the calculation and die. Swifts, then, know how long they will live, and the knowledge rules their parenting.

But what *kind* of knowledge is that? Does it affect the tone of their screaming? Is there a plangent note amongst the older birds? Do the older birds look down at our house on their way back to Africa and say: probably not next year, if the actuaries are right, but it's been a good innings, and I hope our children get this hole? When, in August, they see the coast of Morocco approaching through the haze, do they know that this is the continent where they'll die?

I wonder about such things because, though put like this, these types of thoughts seem preposterously Beatrix Potterish, there plainly is some sort of knowledge of mortality and longevity – even if it is a knowledge encoded so deeply in genes and behaviour that it never wells up into reflection. And yet why do animals seek to avoid annihilation? Doesn't a bird twisting and turning to avoid a peregrine twist and turn because it wants to preserve itself? By which, to be clear, I mean it*self*. Doesn't its eye flare when the talons clutch its back because it*self* is about to be relocated? Isn't *self* one of the basic substrates of at least the biological world – one of the primary reasons for anything doing anything? And don't you need some awareness of the self in order for the self to do the job that evolution intended?

After a nestling's death the parents tend to feed themselves, rather than give all the saved food to the remaining young – which shows that they only starve the young when they are in dire straits themselves. The adults quickly regain the body mass lost by the earlier strenuous parental efforts, and the remaining young typically fledge at weights only slightly below average. All the survivors, adults and nestlings, benefit, and the starved chick hasn't really lost out: when the margins are so small, a tail-ender wouldn't have survived anyway, and would have brought the others to the grave.

Our eaves are ruled by an icily exact utilitarian calculus.

*

And now to those vampires.

They are louse flies (*Crataerina pallida*). They look like crabs, and, relative to the swift's body weight, are about the size that a very respectable edible crab would be to us. They burrow between the adults' feathers, and like to fasten on the neck and belly. In the nestlings they're often on the rump. And they suck blood – lots of it: about five per cent of the adult swift's total blood volume. Every swift nest has them, and some have up to sixteen. Their lives are yoked to the swifts' – though they don't go with them to Africa. When the swifts arrive in the spring, adult louse flies emerge from overwintering pupae, lock on, and start to suck. The birdwatchers might scuttle out of doors to greet the swifts: louse flies scuttle faster and even more hungrily along the rafters to greet them.

Five per cent of lost blood volume is, one would have thought, significant, particularly for a high-functioning aeronautical athlete that spends a lot of its life in the oxygen-depleted air of extreme high altitude. But, strangely, high louse fly loads don't seem to matter. Repeated studies have shown no significant differences in clutch and brood size, nestling growth rate, weight or size at fledging or the number of successfully fledged birds in nests with very different parasite loads.

It's very odd. Perhaps it's a supreme example of co-evolution, in which the amount of food taken by the parasite has been intricately titrated so that there really is no cost to the host – or maybe there's some arcane and currently invisible benefit. Or perhaps there are real costs, but they just don't show up in the traits so far measured. Some suggest that the costs are deferred, so that the nestlings survive (that, after all, is in the louse fly's interest), but how long can a real cost, such as anaemia, be deferred? The newly fledged birds have to fly immediately to

Africa. Perhaps it's relevant to note, here, that louse fly numbers progressively decrease during the swift nesting season, and so it may be that there is time for both adult and young swifts to recover from the massive drainage of earlier in the season before they face the big challenge of migration.

Another mystery is why the swifts put up with louse flies. Wouldn't you pull off a huge edible crab attached to your navel?

I'm inclined to blame the cruciform origin of the swift's splenius capitis – an unusual feature of head and neck musculature that swifts share with hummingbirds. Several strands of the muscle course down from their second vertebra and then interdigitate and cross over one another before attaching to the skull.

The reason for this complex arrangement is obscure, but it may indicate that swifts have traded the ability to move their heads up and down for faster rotation of the head – which may make them better at snatching airborne insects. If so, it may be that swifts simply can't reach the parasites. They could reach the louse flies of other adults and nestlings, of course (though they'd often be hard to see in the gloom of the nest), and the fact that they don't seem to do so might indicate limits to their cognition, or hint that louse flies are indeed an irrelevance or a perverse advantage. Until the puzzle is solved, just reflect that when you watch the swifts whooping through the summer sky, they're carrying a lot of passengers.

I wouldn't mind being a louse fly for a while, though I'd be sorely tempted to hang on and hitch a ride to the Congo.

*

I was woken today as I'd like to be woken always, with the *wheeeeeeeeeeeee!* of the accelerating birds drilling deep into my head. I open my eyes, and the sunlight follows the sound, and before I've time to mourn their passing they're back again, and they come again and again, looping fast and low down our road, and round the next one, and back, and before I've made the morning tea I'm drunk on epiphany and, as usual, casting round for words and finding that they all fail so abjectly that I'm dumb all day and the kids think I'm cross with them. The world and the sky are too full: there's no room up there for my stumbling thoughts.

There is a lot more swift biomass up there than there was yesterday, for many immature non-breeders swept in last night on a wriggling tide of sky-food. They had sidled north. They knew very well that this wasn't going to be their year for parenthood. They may have idled over the Gambia and Senegal, waiting for an optimal tailwind for the Sahara, or danced among the dust-flowers over Marrakesh, which smell of mint and roast chicken.

They came to learn the sky roads, to know what to do when you're caught in a rip current at an altitude of 9,000 feet, and because they had no more choice than the leg of a marionette when the string is pulled.

Above all they came to *plan* – to lay the foundation for their reproductive future. The word 'plan' will raise eyebrows – just as the word 'hope' did – yet no other will do. These immatures didn't come at a time when they thought that, just possibly, there might be a chance of a mate. By the time they arrive it is too late to raise a clutch, even if there were a free hole to do it in. They fly round the territory, learning its landmarks, often in the screaming parties so beloved of swift-enthusiasts, noting the established breeding holes and no doubt wondering whether there might be a vacancy in each one next year.

Sometimes they fly right up to a nest site, braking suddenly in the air and knocking with their wings on the woodwork – an activity called 'banging'. This brings the sitting tenant screeching to the entrance to confirm occupancy. If, by a rare chance, an unoccupied hole is found, that's good news – *but not for this season*. The non-breeding bird might set up home with a bird of the opposite sex. They may even build a nest together. But this is just playing. Sperm will not meet ovum or, if it does, nothing will come of it other than, perhaps, an agreement to do it for real next year.

It's worth pausing to consider what's going on here. And so I want to introduce you properly to the ex-friend who reminded me, at the end of the last chapter, and at high volume, that swifts were *birds*.

I take that reminder seriously, as I take everything he says seriously, because he is a feted evolutionary biologist with hundreds of rightly cited papers and a handful of bracing, rigorous books to his name.

Most biologists I know leave their models of the natural world in the lab when they come home at night. They might spend the day declaring that all altruism is disguised self-interest, that all they want from their spouses are gametes, cooking and a bit of temporary childcare, and that human brains are just chemistry sets, but they don't behave like that when they donate their kidneys, hug their children, write poems to their husbands, and play the Bach Cello suites.

But the ex-friend isn't like that. He's a True Believer. There's a terrifying lack of inconsistency in him. There's no visible seam between the lab and the bedroom. The bedroom's empty now. His wife, he tells me briskly, couldn't take the pace. She's just another of the casualties of natural selection, like the mayfly bodies that clog the rivers on summer days.

The ex-friend likes to think that he means what he says and he says what he means. But everything needs translation. When he says that 'swifts are *birds*', what he really means is that swifts are *just* birds: are *nothing but* birds. And by that he means that swifts are merely machines: that they are nothing but *matter*. And since, for him, matter doesn't matter – and indeed nothing really matters – swifts don't matter either. From which he concludes that looking up into a summer sky and gasping with wonder is a sign of feeble-mindedness which is likely to put you on the wrong side of Darwin.

He is blissfully untroubled by the quantum physicists' mystical queasiness about the nature of matter. They see it as congealed energy, and note that the spin of the electrons in an atom in a swift's toe will affect and be affected by the spin of electrons in an atom in the GN z11 galaxy in the constellation of Ursa Major – the oldest and furthest galaxy in the observable universe, which is 32 billion light years away from the toe. This is because, at the time of the Big Bang, the electrons were close. Once things are close, they affect one another instantaneously and eternally, however far apart they are. And since everything was once close to everything else, everything determines the spin of everything. The universe is an intimate, intimately integrated place.

This is wasted on the ex-friend, because unless you're one of the rare ones who can actually *taste* partial differential equations (and he's not), it's impossible to respond except in the language of the Upanishads or St John's Gospel, and that language, for the ex-friend, is blasphemous obscenity. I asked him once about religion: 'I think I trod in some once', he replied. He sees matter not as sublimated energy, but as lumps of Lego.

On this lovely summer day I didn't want to talk about high-redshift galaxies or the place of swift toes in Hindu cosmology. I just wanted to talk about the bangers and what they were thinking.

'They're not *thinking* at all', sneered the ex-friend. *'I* think. Even *you* sometimes think. But they don't. They just *do.* They just *behave.* A washing-machine doesn't say to itself: "In five minutes I'll go into the drying cycle." It just does it. Birds are the same. So are we, if we had the wit to see it and the honesty to admit it.'

It reminds me of C. S. Lewis's thoughts about animal suffering. Of course painful impulses pass along their nerves. If you stick a pin in a dog's foot it will howl and snatch the foot away. But, he said, they don't suffer in the same way that we do because an essential characteristic of our suffering is the anticipation of more painful impulses in the future. Dogs (he thought) don't have futures; they inhabit the moment and only the moment.

Surely this is nonsense. A dog owned by a cruel master will cringe as it hears the master's feet on the path outside. It knows that in a few moments it will be kicked and beaten. As it cringes it inhabits an imaginary future.

So let's return to the bangers. One has just buzzed the hole in our eaves. I couldn't see what happened, but there was obviously no red carpet. The youngster swerved away with a squawk and scrambled down the road. It had acquired new information about the breeding geography of Oxford. This information, obviously, is useless unless it is retained and assimilated into a revised account of the world.

Nobody doubts that birds have memories. They remember where their nests are, where they've previously found food, and where there's likely to be someone with a gun. They alter their behaviour in the light of those memories: they return to happier hunting grounds, and they avoid the wood where they nearly died. The purpose of the bangers' scouting is to redraw the map of possibilities *for next year.* After a summer of surveying they will fly back to Africa, and through the whole of the autumn, winter and spring they will hold the new map in their minds. When they set off north again next spring the map will be the working document that determines their actions on arrival. I'm warning myself frantically about the dangers of anthropomorphism, but I can't coherently avoid the conclusion that they *plan* in exactly the same way as I do. The sky is screaming with intention; shrieking with agency; responding consciously to contingency.

Consciousness is a sense of self, of subjectivity. The better we get at looking for consciousness, the more we find it. The world seems like a very fertile garden for growing consciousness. Consciousness is everywhere. When the youngsters fly to Africa they must have a picture of *themselves* returning to a particular Oxford hole. To hold, process and plan on the basis of a picture like that is quite clearly to be conscious in the sense that we use the term so proudly of ourselves. They know that they will be different next year from this: they'll be in a position to breed. To note the difference between the self now and the hypothetical self in a year's time demands not just a rudimentary awareness of self, but fairly sophisticated reflection on it. It's beyond most human politicians.

These individuated swift-selves are exuberantly on display at the end of June. All selves show themselves best in relationships – relationships are what Self is *for* – and when the non-breeders arrive the air teems and throbs with relationship. The screaming parties are just that: parties at which everyone screams. Whatever the merely biological benefits of the screaming parties (and has anything, ever, been *merely* biological?), no one who has seen and heard one of them (with the tragic exception of the ex-friend) can doubt that the overwhelming reason for joining them is that they are colossal fun.

At dawn and dusk the main members of the twilight-ascent groups are the non-breeders. They may be exploring the lines where the different layers of the atmosphere fold into one another; they may be collecting and comparing barometric information. But what they're really there for, beyond our sight, but perhaps not so far beyond our understanding, is gossip.

'They're with us now', breathed my lovely swift-loving neighbour. 'Ours until August. Such a privilege.' Yes, a privilege indeed. And of course the core of the colony, the breeding pairs and their offspring, are indeed here until they leave in August. The non-breeders, too, are closely affiliated to the colony, but they seem to be much less local than the breeders. If the weather closes in the breeders will just sit miserably, but relatively safe, in the nest hole. The non-breeders have only the air, and if the air loses its temper they may have to run.

For swifts near the coast, it makes sense to run out to sea. At night there's a better chance of rising currents over sea than over land. The land makes for unreliable air. Land air is full of potholes and mounds and stomach-churning troughs. But the summer sea tends to be more stable. Its temperature is more constant. It doesn't slap the air around like the land.

Sit on the east coast of England on a late June or July evening and, as the light fades, you're likely to see groups of common swifts flying purposefully out to sea. When the land slackens its clutch on the air, they'll start to drift up, and there they will stay until dawn or later, feathers fluffed against the fog, half a brain asleep and the other watching the circling stars and the lights of the container ships on their way to Harwich, and listening to the boom of the horns.

Sometimes the weather convenes vast gatherings. The largest ever daily count of swifts in Britain was in 2020 at Gibraltar Point in Lincolnshire. There were more than 46,000. I'd have given my right arm to have been there.

These gatherings show how *geographical* their lives are. On the day of the Lincolnshire gathering there was a large, bird-chewing depression moving from the north-east of Scotland towards Scandinavia, and probably shoving Scandinavian swifts before it. So here they were in Lincolnshire, marking time, climbing high, peering north over the clouds, and waiting for the depression to move south-east, leaving them room to cut clockwise round it and back into Norway. David Lack thought that these sorts of weather movements might easily involve journeys of a thousand miles.

These huge collections aren't murmurations. There's no co-ordinated movement of the flock of the kind so admired in starlings and many other species – movements, so some say, so fast as to be impossible on the basis of ordinary eye-brain-wing connection; movements faster than the speed of passage of impulses along bird nerves. There's no neurological freakiness here, in which individual will and individual physiology are overridden, and each bird becomes assimilated into a gigantic super-organism.

In the heart of the Lincolnshire 46,000, each bird made its own way and its own decisions. They are only ever themselves.

From early June the swifts in Israel and Palestine start to leave, and by the middle or end of July, the last late breeders will go. But already in June the Swift-Wide-Web begins to take on a different tone. Mostly it's still the bubbling rhapsodies of the Europeans, but now there's the occasional dissonant note. 'Fewer today.' 'Our skies are haemorrhaging.' 'Our nest is empty. If anyone in Eilat sees them, tell them to come home at once.' 'What's wrong with Jerusalem? Still plenty of food here.' For many in the Levant, the winter starts in June.

To us in Europe, this seems bad manners, poor taste. Like talking about cremation in the middle of a jolly summer picnic.

18th June   3rd bird prospecting box 1

July

Swifts don't scream. They cluck gently like lazy farm hens scratching round in the yard. That's what you'll hear if you slow down their calls to a tenth of the speed. Slow down to a quarter of the speed, and you'll hear a wavering, tremulous aria, like a great northern diver on a cold lake. Since swifts live their lives far more than ten times faster than I live mine, I'm inclined to think that the real sound of swifts, to other swifts, is a low, deep, broken muttering – the sound of old men in deep armchairs after a long lunch.

Today, getting up from my own armchair and shambling across the room at about half a mile an hour, I stubbed my toe. As I was cursing, I heard what I now know to be the muttering of swifts outside, and I looked up to see long streaks of black hurtling (sauntering, really, I thought) past the bedroom windows of the terraced houses in our street. One of the streaks bent off and snapped: a swift had gone to its nest under the tiles.

*

My own bruised toe set me thinking about the toes of that nesting swift. It has been calculated that a swift enters its nestbox at about 43 miles an hour. When the entrance hole is big enough it flies straight in, and it must land on its feet – there's little room to spread the wings and brake. The forces on the toes must be enormous. Tigges concluded that there must be a 'seemingly impossible' pressure of 40 kilogrammes – that's nearly 90 pounds.

I've held a swift's feet. They're long, thin, scaly and savage, like the little useless hands of bipedal dinosaurs. Ninety pounds? Never: yet another example of swifts laughing in Newton's face.

Let's say that a swift weighs 40 grammes. I weigh about 95 kilogrammes – that's the weight of 2,375 swifts. It's not quite so simple, of course, but if one just scales up a force on the foot of a forty-gramme bird to the equivalent force on the foot of a fat man waddling across a room, that's like having a nine-and-a-half-tonne weight on my toes. Swifts have big lorries roll over their toes many times a day during the season – all to feed the children.

'They bring out the best in us all, don't they?' says my lovely neighbour. 'They remind us that we all live in one world; that nations are ridiculous. And they make us look up – away from the moment, away from our own concerns.'

I badly want to agree with her. But I spent an hour this morning sitting on our front doorstep. It's a great place for swift-watching. Long before it was time for me to take the children to school the swifts were being yanked along between the layers of air (they always seem to be pulled, never to drive themselves forward, and they go too fast to be going *through* the air) just above the heads of the people walking down the street.

Those heads, then, were part of one of the most thrilling celebrations of life that, so far as we know, the universe holds. There was nothing subtle about it. My eardrums sometimes hurt with the sort of pain I long for them always to have. Yet not one head lifted. Not one.

This makes me feel bad things about humans. Things of which I am very ashamed. I am angry – angry at the ingratitude of the unlifted heads; I am sad – sad that so peerless an opportunity for joy has been missed; I am worried – for if humans won't respond to *that*, how can they be expected to care about anything that really matters? I am ashamed to be a member of my species, and ashamed to be thinking such things about people I know to be better than me – to be generous, kind and altruistic; and I am baffled that one can be so generous, kind and altruistic and yet carry on looking at the pavement. What sort of creatures are we?

There: swifts have created division. They don't just cut through the air, they carve people into categories. It would be hard to be married to someone who didn't love swifts, and I'm angrily fearful that my children will carry on looking at the road. I'm fierce with them: 'How can you not look up!'

It's the sort of summer day that makes even me feel kind towards England. We're going swimming in the river a few miles downstream. My wife drives us there. It's not safe for me to drive in high summer, because *they* are always up there somewhere, and my eyes go with them.

We park, and then the swifts explode out of a ball of light above an old oak. A lush breeze is pressing waves of insects from the meadow against the trees, and then the waves rear up and climb for a while before curling in and crashing back down onto the cows, and the swifts are barrelling through this entomological surf, rolling in it, harvesting air-krill from the spindrift.

We jump from a tree into the water and pull the skin of the water over our heads, and when I stick my head out again there's a swift a couple of feet away, stooping to snatch a whirring beetle, and the children are laughing and the river is pouring from them and everything is shining and it's all too much.

That night we take our supper down to our local lake and sit trailing our legs in the water. There's a band of mist over the far, windward side of the lake. It's a new hatch of midges, and the swifts are hacking through it, their bodies pale with the insect wings.

These are probably local breeders, and this is a crucial time for them. They have rapidly growing nestlings who themselves need to be inter-continentally fit in the next four weeks.

I do some more of my unscientific back-of-the-envelope calculations to try to wrap my head around the sort of thing that a swift is. David Lack recorded 42 meals brought to the young in a day, which would probably be around 50 grammes of insects – around 20,000 individual insect bodies, all bound together in saliva from the glands that first started to swell, in anticipation of parenthood, when the birds were still over the Congo.

Twenty-five grammes per parent is 63 per cent of the parent's bodyweight. It's like me lugging back from the corner shop (or perhaps a corner shop 60 miles away, since swifts may be forced far from home for the necessary calories), 60 kilogrammes of groceries every day, after 10,000 individual grabs from the shelves. And the adults have to feed themselves too.

Adult swifts have quite rigorously divided parenting time and 'me' time. In good weather they'll hunt for the children as soon as the insects start moving in the morning – which might, depending on the latitude, be quite late, and the children will have much of the big insect haul in the afternoon and the evening. But whatever the weather, the adults hunt less frantically for a while around noon. This is probably when they're looking after themselves; hunting to eat; perhaps washing in a cloud; perhaps climbing with the youngsters and remembering how it was before domestic responsibilities pressed hard – like dads wistfully playing football in the park; perhaps looking after their feathers, turning their heads in the air and lifting their wings and running the plumes through their beaks to reattach the Velcro hooks loosened by gusts of wind and the attrition of the nestbox.

Margins are tight. Oxford might look like a land flowing with milk and honey, but the swifts are generally on a knife-edge. During the first three weeks after hatching, the parents eat the nestlings' faecal sacs (the females eat significantly more than the males). It's probably not mainly about hygiene, but about nutrition and hydration. Those infant guts aren't completely efficient, and there's still quite a lot of water and nutrients in the faeces. It may, too, be a strategy to suppress appetite – to fill up the parent with something so that she's more inclined to feed the young rather than herself; a way of triumphing over her baser, more selfish nature; a way to mute the voice of the filicidal July algorithm that tells her to save herself, kill the children, and live to breed again next year.

At about four in the afternoon, one 12th July, the crew of a survey vessel 151 nautical miles off the coast of Surinam noticed a black swift flying around the ship. It stayed with them for about an hour, resting on the ship's updraft, gliding smoothly. It had a white chin, and the biologists on board identified it as a white chinned swift, well known from Surinam, Guyana, Venezuela and northern Brazil. They posted a photo on a blog, and thought no more about it.

A year later the Cornell Ornithology lab got in touch. It's not a white chinned swift at all, they said: it's *Apus apus,* the common swift – possibly a juvenile, because of the pale fringes on the forehead.

It seemed impossible. Though they have a reputation for vagrancy, and have been recorded on Ascension Island, Bermuda and very, very occasionally in North America, common swifts don't get to South America. Yet there it was, its well-defined chin patch damp in the salty mangrove wind, its lower belly scaly and reptilian. How on earth?

The biologists had their own ideas. They thought that it had left its breeding area in Europe (though a juvenile wouldn't have bred that year) and become disoriented on its way back to Africa. They noted that in late June and early July the North Atlantic was a scary place. There was a tropical cyclone in the western North Atlantic, and a storm blowing west filled the Atlantic with African dust as far as Florida.

They speculated that the swift lost its way somewhere in the region of Senegal or Mauritania, before making its planned turn into the interior of Africa. It's about 2,542 miles from there to the boat rocking off Surinam, and if the swift travelled confidently in the wrong direction, with the wind behind it, it might have made 186 miles per day, arriving at the boat after about fourteen days of lonely, foodless flying, looking down through suspended Saharan sand, blinking out the grit, its nictitating membrane perhaps pulled down over its eyes to stop them being rasped, watching vainly for beetles and other swifts, seeing only a very occasional wandering tubenose coasting over the wave crests (for most seabirds were still at their breeding sites), and, once every couple of days a distant container ship tunnelling towards Rio or Luanda, full of trucks and TVs. Once in a while it must have climbed to drink from a cloud.

I imagine that when it saw the boat it smelt land too, and then there were occasional small spiders from the tangled forests a couple of hundred miles away, and it began to wonder if it had reached Africa at last – a mistake rather like Columbus's. There were humans on the boat. It recognised humans from its time in Europe. They lived in places where there were other swifts and plenty of insects, and so it gratefully joined them for a while.

The more I think about this swift, the more baffling its story is. If it had arrived off the coast of South America a few weeks later I wouldn't be scratching my head. But assuming that the biologists' reconstruction of events is right (and it seems very reasonable), what was the bird doing in Senegal or Mauritania at the end of *June*?

True, the non-breeding juveniles and failed breeders

tend to leave before the breeders – there's a big exodus of these birds from England in mid-July. Yes, in more southern latitudes, where the swifts arrive earlier, they may be gone rather earlier too. But on the way back to Africa there is no rush, as there is in the spring. To be all the way to West Africa by the end of June? That's odd.

Swifts leave the Middle East before they leave Europe. The Israeli swifts start to leave in June, and all, bar stragglers, are gone by the middle or end of July. Could the Surinam bird be from the Middle East? It seems very unlikely. They take more or less the same route back to central Africa that they took on their spring migration – so across Sinai or the Red Sea, probably down the Nile valley for a while, and then south-west to the eastern Congo, and to Zambia and Angola. If the Surinam bird was one of them, we'd have to suppose that it went all the way to the West African coast (and why would it?), had the misfortune to be bundled up in a tropical storm and hurled out to sea, and (despite having found its way from the Middle East to Africa) was so lacking in navigational ability that it couldn't tell east from west, or so lacking in flying ability that it was completely helpless in the teeth of the wind.

It all seems so improbable that I'm tempted to opt for a supernatural explanation instead. I can't help wondering, though, whether there's a population of non-migratory birds and probably juvenile birds that over-winter, at least sometimes, in Africa, choosing not to spend all those resources on a dangerous, costly and sexless trip to Europe, but instead to guzzle and grow silky sleek on the entomological smorgasbord of Africa. If one of those navigationally naive birds were sucked by a cyclone into the Atlantic, it might, once out of sight of land, become disastrously confused.

What became of it? It can never have found its way back to Africa. It must have reached the rainforest of north-eastern South America and lived out its life there. It would have found plenty to eat. Surviving in South America, for an insectivore, is very like surviving in central Africa. But swifts are supremely social birds, and its loneliness must have been, and may still be, crushing: the loneliness of the last of any species, looking pointlessly for a mate or just a screaming partner, paralysed by sexual frustration.

I'd love to believe, but I can't, that its compass gradually recalibrated and that one spring it set out to the north-east and saw, with a thrill of recognition, a group of sickle-winged hunters pausing to feed on the flies rising from the heaps of fish guts in Nouakchott's fishing harbour; and that it saluted them and they saluted it, and that they went on together to a castellated thirteenth-century tower in the Alhambra, threaded with tight, dry, rat-free passages looking out on a gentle courtyard owned by a starling-hating naturalist, and with blue hills beyond.

The adult birds keenly inspect the new laid eggs. Any sign of a crack, and the offending egg will be rolled out of the hole to smash on the ground next to our bikes. Inside the surviving eggs the chicks come slowly into focus: buds become limbs, shadows become bone.

When they hatch they are blind. They know day from night because in the day there is a dark pink haze in front of them, and in the night there is not, and in the night both parents are there under the eaves with them, but there is no food.

Their bodies, inside and out, begin to shift around themselves, like the tectonic pieces of the continents shuffling into place. Their necks start to retreat into their chests, their eyes to swivel and open, their bellies to flatten, their cloacas to creep round off their backs. Dark-grey cylinders, like shotgun cartridges, rise out of their wings and press out. Their toes start off in opposed pairs like songbirds', but swifts don't perch, and the rear toes swing round to point forwards with the others. The translucent, paper-thin skin thickens and darkens, and beneath it is a shifting archipelago of yellow fat, its islands swelling and joining when the weather is good, and thinning and parting when the rain falls.

Their first sensations are the warmth of their parents' feathers, the metallic stickiness of crushed beetles forced into their gullets, the drawl of the rain, the occasional blast of deadly heat when the afternoon sun makes an oven of the eaves, and the littlenesses and meannesses and joys and kindnesses of our house: the music, the battles, the games and the bedtime stories.

The first sounds the nestlings will hear when they hatch, other than a low purr from their parent, will be Rachel and Jonny fighting over territory and stuff. They will hear big, loud claims: 'That's mine', 'No it's not: Jamie gave it to me.' 'Yes, but then he said he hated you and took it off you and gave it to me.' It's a good introduction to the world of warring, neoliberal humans. The swifts will know all about the DRC before they hear the gunfire.

They'll hear Jamie scraping his fiddle, and Tom moodily strumming, and Jonny working out his jazz chords, and Rachel singing Taylor Swift rather than Common Swift to herself, and me sighing and cursing and asking hopelessly if they haven't had enough of Stephen Bloody Fry reading Harry Potter and shouldn't they try *King Lear* instead because they might just find there's more in it, and my saintly wife Mary coming in as peacekeeper and soothing everyone with juice and tea and buns. And from outside they'll hear the murmur of genteel dispute about bins and boundaries, and cars trundling up the road towards the shopping centre that has gridlocked Oxford and can't be helping the availability of airborne insects.

Once in a while they might hear my panicked breathing as I hang out of the window with my face close to the nest-hole entrance, hoping that I'll see them eye to eye and become part of their world.

A newly hatched swift weighs around 2.75 grammes. In good weather it will increase its weight twenty-fold by its fourth week, hitting the important threshold of 56 grammes in its fourth week. If a human neonate of 3.5 kilogrammes increased its weight at the same rate, it would weigh 70 kilogrammes – 11 stones – at a month old.

However lean the year, all surviving fledglings will, eventually, be heavier than their parents. They will also have to lose weight themselves in the last week before they launch into the sky. The fat under their skin and around their liver has been their insurance policy against the risk of a disastrous summer, but now the policy is ripped up as a more urgent kind of mathematics comes into play.

This is the mathematics of flight. Life in the air is about the ratio of lift to drag. This ratio will increase by 9.8 per cent in the last week of shivering weight loss in the roof (as it probably would for me if I fasted for a month). The loss of body mass reduces the minimum power speed, the maximum range speed, and the maximum range power: those, for the moment, are not the priority. Their time will come – probably, I guess, somewhere in North Africa in a few weeks' time.

For now, though, a potent aerodynamic synergy is developing: every moment the wings push further out from the body, and every moment the body weight falls, which means that the lift–drag ratio rises, making it easier for a novice to remain airborne, and increasing manoeuvrability. These are vital. Without them the bird would crash into rooftops as it blundered through the suburbs on its maiden flight, and it would starve: inexperienced hunters have to laboriously chase insects that their parents take with the slight tilt of a feather.

Flight speed might matter for migration, but it's not as crucial as it was in the spring. The young swifts can and will get fitter and stronger on the way. Walkers who start the Pennine Way flabby and soft end it lithe and hard. It's like that for the young swifts. In any event they may not start for Africa immediately after leaving the nest, but have a gentle flying apprenticeship in the home territory. Once aloft they continue to evolve physically as flying machines. Fledglings' wings are shorter than those of adults, and probably continue to get longer after the fledgling leaves the nest. That's what happens with bats, and one can well imagine how shorter wings might be easier to use until the bird gets used to flying – just as short skis are best for novices. Swifts are equipped at the start with entry-level wings, and gradually, on the way to Africa, they upgrade.

The balance between body mass and wing length and strength is crucial. If it's not right, the young swift will fall like a stone and lie amongst the rejected eggs under our bikes until it's mangled by a cat. Sometimes they don't get it right. I've got a couple of miscalculating youngsters pickled in jam-jars in my study. But mostly they do, and they get it right by doing press-ups.

From around four weeks of age they partly extend their wings and press down on the floor, trying to lift the body and the feet clear. At first they can't manage it at all, but they gradually get better, and by the time they're ready to fly, they can hold it for ten seconds or more. The ten seconds is hard-wired into them: it tells them that their lift–drag ratio is up to the job.

They can go.

Swiftlets 20 days old

August

I've tried not to notice that August is coming. But the signs are ominously insistent: school summer plays, ads for last-minute charter flights to Ibiza, reduced significance of the boundaries of the Oxford swift colonies, with groups from different colonies beginning to mingle, and many more screaming parties.

No one knows (where have we heard that before?) why there are more screaming parties. Perhaps the swifts are cementing old alliances from within their own colonies and forging new ones from further afield. Perhaps they want company on the long voyage ahead; perhaps (and particularly if they haven't bred this year) they're taking this once-in-a-season opportunity to have a look at the other territories with a view to staking an early claim for a vacant hole next spring; perhaps they're getting a last taste of sociation before being swallowed up by the sky; perhaps they're increasing the chances of knowing someone when they're all mixed up together in Africa over the winter; perhaps they're gathering intelligence and opinions about the optimal time to leave.

I doubt, myself, that the reason is logistical, simply because swifts leave in such a piecemeal way. If there were some compelling meteorological or other reason to leave at a particular time you'd expect them to leave close together. But they don't.

It's hard to get a clear picture of what they *do* do. Some people say that immature birds often leave before the breeders, particularly if the weather's bad. That may make sense: they've no investment in Oxford this time round, and the world is their oyster. Some say that they leave in the same sort of period as the breeders, but towards the end of that period, so as to assert for longer their title to the nest hole they hope to occupy next May. Certainly young swallows spend a good deal of time scouting before they head south – and this seems to pay dividends: early broods, which have more time to look around, tend to have a better chance of finding a place in the following season.

But what am I doing? It's only just August and I'm already imagining them gone. Typical. Afraid to get too close for fear of the pain of loss. So I slam down the books and close the file of scientific papers and switch off the bloody laptop and run out to the field next to the tree where once, swaying in a warm wind, I found myself in the middle of a flock of trawling swifts; found myself staring into a grey mouth full of nymphs. And I sidestep around the neatly tied plastic bags of dog shit left by people who are far less comprehensible even than swifts, and fling myself down and look up and pray for a swift epiphany that never comes, and then head back to my study, and as soon as I've sat down and started to type there they are outside my window because that is the way things are.

*

When the fledglings leave the nest, it's the most dramatic transition in the natural world. It's a shift between states of being; like the direct sublimation of a solid to a gas. There's nothing *biological* that's like it in any way, other than death – the departure of a soul. Homer writes about the soul of a slain warrior coming out through his nose and returning to the ground. Swift fledglings come out from a nostril-like hole in the body of a house and become part of the air. Beside this the metamorphosis of a caterpillar into a butterfly is as miraculous as a VAT return.

The fledglings know that it's like dying – and might, if they've misinterpreted their press-ups, actually *be* dying.

For a few days before leaving, the fledgling shuffles to the entrance of the hole, looks out and down and around, and then, many, many times, turns round and goes back into the safe dark, and comes out again, and goes back, until finally, one morning, usually before eight, and always while the parents are away (dying is something you have to do alone), it topples into the air. This first journey might be the last. If it's not the last, it won't touch anything on terra firma, except briefly, for at least two, and possibly four years. Once in the air it knows straight away that the air is what it is *for;* that the wood of the eaves, which seemed so solid and reliable, is as misty and insubstantial as a dream.

It may stretch its wings, perfect its turns, scream with the others, and build its muscle around the home territory. It may watch as its younger or more nervous siblings discover, too, that the eaves are a snare, an illusion, a delusion and fling themselves off and die to the dirty, shitty mess of solids. Or it may turn south (how?) and head up and away (how?), to a place to which it's never been before (how?), thousands and thousands of miles away (how?), there to meet or not to meet, in the sultry wet, the nestlings it elbowed and pecked, and the parents who nearly killed themselves for it. Whatever it does, it won't return to the nest this year, or the next, or very possibly ever. If it returns, it will return as the proud victor in the battle to reproduce, inheriting its dead or debilitated parents' estate, though not as of right.

But the parents return to the nest after the offspring have gone. They look like human empty-nesters feel. They look poignantly at the old bedroom. They move things pointlessly around. They are stunned and disoriented. They sleep in the old nest, though they could be dozing above the clouds. They catch up on sleep, and feed in preparation for Africa, but there's no sense of smug triumphalism about them. They look dispossessed – as if they don't know what life is for any more. And then, up to around three and a half weeks after the young, in a patch of good weather, they gird up their loins and depart south themselves.

I've never seen them go. I'm too scared to watch. It tends to be quite early in the morning or at dusk. A flock gathers and screams and spirals up and up. Some of them have just risen to say goodbye to the others, and peel off and return, but the main party, right on the edge of vision and right over the edge of understanding, dives into a cloud as if to wash off the Oxford smut, and heads out to the south-west.

'Why do they go?' asks that lovely neighbour, looking forlornly up into the silence. She means it, as I would mean it, as self-rebuke. Oxford and she have been weighed in the balance by the most exacting judges, and found wanting.

Like all worthwhile questions, this one can be asked and answered on any number of levels.

The swifts have to go eventually, before the sun leaves. Unless you're a waterbird these are mean, sterile islands in the winter.

Apparently some swallows are trying to overwinter here. They'll die, but some vestiges of their pioneer genes will linger in more prudent birds and rear up again to give us winter swallows when climate chaos turns the northern winter into a sauna. No doubt the same will happen with swifts.

But the questions 'Why right now?' and 'What's the trigger for departure?' aren't so easy.

It used to be thought that it was the light, and that once there were fewer than seventeen hours of light the swifts went. It's not so. The further south you go, the faster the sun retreats, but the pattern of retreat doesn't match the pattern of the swifts' departure.

Nor is it the food. Gilbert White, writing in 1769, concluded that swifts 'are supported by some sorts of high-flying gnats, scarabs, or *phaloenae,* that are of short continuance; and that the short stay of these strangers is regulated by the defect of their food.' True, in a typical August there aren't the gargantuan insect hatches of earlier in the summer, and gritty beetles tend to replace succulent bugs (I imagine it as a change from rump steak to beans on dry toast). But you can live happily on beans on toast, and there are plenty of calories in the sky well into the autumn. No: it is simply that England has done its job. It is a brood chamber, and once the brood has gone there's no reason to stay other than, perhaps, to recuperate for a while from the stresses of parenthood, to take a last sentimental look at the nursery, and to replenish the fat store to keep the engine turning on the journey ahead. They don't even *need* to do that: the parents of late broods are off as soon as the children fly the nest.

There's no kind way to break it to the neighbour: the swifts have used her. This isn't their home.

I try to be away when they leave, to avoid that sudden sickening emptiness. When they're gone from 'our' colony they're gone, and there's no denying it, and the sight of the odd migrant overhead just serves to rub it in: it's not one of ours.

Into the hole left by the swifts pours all sorts of poison: panic at the speed of the world's turning and the creep of the dark; hypochondria; tetchiness and mooning self-absorption. Now that the sky's not screeching with joy I can hear the steady tread of dissolution and despair. The garden smells of roses, I'm told, but I smell decay. I am cold in the hottest sun.

'They're *birds,* for Christ's sake', the ex-friend reminds me. 'All that's happened is that some dickie-birds are tweeting somewhere else. You need urgent and professional help.'

It's harder now, with the kids around, but sometimes, in the middle of August, I sling clothes and binoculars into a rucksack and go off in pursuit. Sometimes I go to southern Spain, for they tend to funnel through the Straits of Gibraltar.

I tend to go by train because I like trains, and because I feel that it's only right to be looking always *up* towards the swifts. It wouldn't be proper to look down on them from a plane – though I've applied that principle very inconsistently over the years.

When I get to Spain I go to the same cliff-top that I sit on in the spring, and watch for the flickering that says that they're up there, and unscientifically muse that that's a Portuguese swift, and that's a Dane, and that's clearly French, and Parisian to boot. But I've been there when they've stopped coming, and that's bad, really bad. Colm Tóibín says that the only good thing about a parent dying is that it can't happen again. Going to Gibraltar can be inviting a second bereavement, just as you're hypersensitive from the first.

'Pathological', says the ex-friend. 'Someone should write you up. There's a PhD in your neuroses.'

More often, though, I go to Greece, for there, well into the autumn, there are swifts to be seen, and they seem more at home there than anywhere else in Europe – as I am myself. But when I go to Greece in the autumn I never, ever pack my binoculars, for I've a nasty suspicion, that I don't have the stomach to confirm, that they're not common swifts, *Apus apus,* around that tower in Ouranopoli, or hawking round the Castro in Monemvasia, or slaloming between silver olives on the hill above Areopolis. Better not to know. Let me hang onto the delusion: it doesn't do anyone any harm.

'Except yourself, of course', sneers the ex-friend. 'Better to confront the terrible possibility that they might be pallid swifts.'

The swifts dribbling across the Straits of Gibraltar aren't just going to *Africa.* They're going to specific African places. Individual birds have their own favourite routes and their own preferred destinations within Africa. It is also becoming clear that, while the Congo and Liberia in spring might be a melting pot for swifts from many African locations, going to many European destinations, African swift populations are organised quite rigidly by reference to latitude. The swifts breeding furthest to the south in Europe winter further to the south in Africa (in relatively cooler places like Mozambique and Zambia), and those breeding furthest to the north winter further to the north (in relatively hotter, equatorial places). That might not seem terribly surprising. It might seem as if there's a fixed length of tolerable migration, and that a swift that has come from Norway might not want to head as far south as one that's come from Sicily. But there's more to it than that: the southern-breeding, southern-wintering swifts are larger than the northern-breeding, northern-wintering birds, and also raise more young and arrive earlier in the wintering areas that have the highest seasonal variation in greenness.

The southern birds look like a glossy, fit, pampered elite who have made good choices about where to spend the summer, and are reaping the benefits. Who, after, all, would choose to live on herbicide-drenched flea-beetles from rape fields inside the M25 when you could live on organic nymphs from a thyme-scented mountain in Arcadia? In Darwin's world the winner takes it all: food, children, Mediterranean view.

And that may indeed be what's happening here. It may be that there is strong competition for nesting sites in the luxurious southern regions, and that big, strong, pushy individuals get to breed there, producing, on the easy pickings, big, strong, pushy children who will inherit the estate in due course, seeing off, as their parents did, any puny pretenders with northern accents who aspire to move up the property ladder. That would mean that the northern breeders are indeed second-class evolutionary citizens, living on the leavings of the southern birds.

There are a couple of ways to defend the honour of the northern birds. One might say that they're tough specialised survivors who have evolved a smaller body size because smaller bodies need less energy and are therefore able to survive in the colder, meaner fringelands of Europe where the big-bodied southern softies would perish. Or that those smaller bodies are better suited to higher equatorial temperatures.

So, yes, the northern birds are impressive. It's hard to raise children in the cold and the heat, yet they do. But who's the winner? Who's the best? In Darwin's frigidly neoliberal world I'm afraid it's plain. What is success? It's not making the best of a bad job; not playing adroitly the hand that fate has dealt you. It's output; GDP; lifetime reproductive success. The southern birds take the prize.

The reproductive feats of those doughty northern birds, though, mean that common swifts as a species look tremendously impressive. The sky isn't one place: it's full of well-demarcated niches, each requiring a different set of physiological traits and behavioural solutions. *Apus apus* is a brilliant exploiter of many different niches. The southern softies, if they've got any general swift-pride, can bask in the reflected glory of their despised northern cousins.

It's said that wintering swifts are silent. Certainly there aren't the rampaging screaming parties – which might mean that the parties are to do with colonial bonding or the assertion of territorial claims. But often in Africa they are very high – well beyond any human ear. Throughout the winter they do their twilight climbs, and so if, which seems likely, those are at least in part *conversational* groups, it's hard to believe they're mute.

Can any bird that's so intensely relational in Europe change its personality and habits when it crosses the Mediterranean? It'd be like a garrulous, giggling, tipsy teenager morphing into a Trappist nun as soon as she stepped onto the tarmac at Casablanca airport.

Many birds – and there's no reason to suppose that swifts are an exception – can hear sounds separated by less than two thousandths of a second. Humans only hear sounds as distinct if they're separated by a tenth of a second or more. Put another way, if the purpose of vocalisation is to transmit information, bird sounds potentially convey fifty times as much information per unit time as the sounds that are at the limit of our resolution. A one-hour lecture delivered at the limit of our resolution would be heard and assimilated by a bird in one minute twelve seconds. Those jubilant, momentary squirts of sound that should make you lift your heads contain the data on many pages of a human book.

The swifts I've heard in the autumn skies on the edge of Europe are far from silent. Does the sea really strike them dumb for the next nine months?

Nothing else is visibly migrating at the moment. The cuckoos have gone already, a few weeks ago, but only they and the swifts *use* Europe as a reproductive tool in quite such a business-like way, staying only as long as the graphs and formulae say they have to stay; not bonding with the place. Perhaps swifts evoke such a passionate, monomaniacal response from us *because* they don't love us back.

In September and October other birds will be queuing up on the Gibraltar runway to take off for Africa. They will fumble into the air and scramble through it. You'll be able to see how they're ruffled and tumbled; you'll be able to hear the creaking effort as they flap and fluster. If you've been watching swifts it won't look like flying at all, but like the panicky splashing of a child learning to swim.

But now, in southern Spain, the sky is the swifts'. Hot gulls stab a pie on the beach. In the bushes behind me little brown birds with twitching eyes and panting beaks are watching for cats. Jackdaws clink like clashing cups, and crows check the pulse of everything they see, hoping there might soon be a corpse.

Offshore the waves are chasing each other up and down and round and round like children who've had too much sugar, and the air is a mess of eddying pools. To make anything of air like this, let alone to make headway, the air has to be your place. Swifts are circling as calmly as fat ducks on a village millpond.

The swifts *use* Europe, yes, but once Europe has done its job as an incubator, they don't always bolt straight for Africa. For Africa isn't really home either. The air is home, and there's air in Europe, too, even if it's not as interesting or as clean as the briny air of Angola or the fermenting marrow air of Benin. So some of them hang around.

Anyone who doubts that birds are individuals should look at the patchy reports of the bird-watchers and the articles of the systematic swift-trackers. 'Three overhead today in Nice'. 'Toulon: A small group heading south-west at noon.' 'They're still with us – just – in the Dordogne.' 'Looks as if they've set up home for the winter in Grenada' (they haven't). Always with the resignation and delusional hope that I have.

The tracking data look similarly patchy. Many Swedish swifts stop in Iberia for about a fortnight before heading to the Sahara. And many don't. Some Danish swifts arrive in the Sahel on 1 September. And some don't. There's immense variation. The time taken for Swedish swifts to get from Sweden to the border of Niger and Chad varies between 4 and 72 days. The total time before they're back in the general wintering area is an average of 69 days, but that varies between 30 and 99.

It's an unhurried journey: the 69 days is just 30 days of travelling and 39 days of stopovers (of more than 2 days). These stopovers are more evenly distributed than they are in the spring, and the whole process is more relaxed than in the spring – when the average travelling time for Swedish swifts is 29 days, with a spread of 18 to 34. In terms of distance, too, there's more meandering in the autumn. The autumn migration is, on average, 53 per cent longer than the direct route would be, compared to 43 per cent longer in the spring. The spring detour is mostly due to the great Liberian pause – a feeding stop. The autumn pauses have much more of a sightseeing feel about them. The speeds are very different in autumn and spring. In the autumn the speed, if one includes stopovers, is 105 miles per day, and 213 miles if stopovers are excluded. In the spring it's 208 miles per day without stopovers, and 291 miles per day with them.

There: a breathless race through lots of figures, the result of thousands of meticulous hours in labs and at computers and in stuffy swift towers by clever people. Always, as I've been trawling the scientific literature, I've felt an uneasy dissonance. I look down at the page, puzzle out the graph, try to unknot the equations. And then I look up and see grace, power and redemption, and I do not know how the pages relate to the surging sky. I do not know what comes first – the charts or the grace. I do not know how much acceleration, stamina, or oxygen-carrying capacity of the haemoglobin could be lost without stopping a swift being what it is. I do not know if they would stop being redemptive if they didn't stop off in Liberia. I suppose this is all just another way of saying that, like every human who has ever lived (apart from the ex-friend), I am confused and troubled by the mysterious relationship of matter and spirit.

As I sit on the Spanish cliff, dreamily staring out to sea, I notice one of the waiters talking with a seven-year-old urchin. The waiter's pointing towards me, and giving careful instruction. The little lad nods slowly, as if he's learning his lines, opens the door, and walks slowly across the terrace. He speaks basic and heavily accented English, and he's obviously on commission.

'Do you know, mister, how to tell the mister birds from the lady birds?' He points up. He's been told that I'm here for the swifts. Of course I don't. Nobody does. Males and females look identical to human eyes. I shake my head and turn my eyes back over the straits. But he won't be shaken off so easily.

'You want to know, mister? I'll tell you.'

'Go on then.'

'At the end of the song the lady bird is slower than the mister bird.'

It's not a bad summary. It's worth a Euro.

The trill at the end of the scream is indeed just about the only way to tell males and females apart – but the human ear can't do it. The gap between the notes of the female trill is

25 milliseconds or more; for the male it's 20 milliseconds or less. To our gross sensibilities those differences are auditorily invisible. To the birds they are barn-door sexual stereotypes of a blatant and old-fashioned kind. Real men = a time lapse of < 20 milliseconds.

And this sets me wondering again about the difference in the intensity with which I and the swifts live our respective lives. If there's that much significance for them in a five-millisecond gap, what symphonic glories or diabolical outrages might there be in the revving of an engine or the whisper of a tree – let alone in the strains of the Andalusian music that's trickling out of the bar. What would a swift make of the Bach B Minor Mass?

The swifts circling here are waiting for a tailwind, it's said. Is it just that?

September

Migration, by our standards, seems mad. So much effort for such an apparently marginal return. We wouldn't do it, and so we think that nothing else should. We forget that the main characteristic of humans is our ability to manipulate our environment; to change it to suit us; to bring heat and light in midwinter by lighting fires; to dry meat and fruit, and so have plentiful food when the caribou have moved on and when there are no berries on the trees. This skill means that we never really live where and when we are. Since the times of the earliest humans we have lived in self-created worlds, relatively immune to geography, and able to slow down the sinister creep of the clock.

We have forgotten that this is a very unusual characteristic, that most creatures are embedded in their place and their time, vulnerable to them as we are not, and that if a non-human wants to live in perpetual heat and light they will have to follow the heat and light, whatever that takes, rather than pulling them out of a bag.

Migration seems particularly ridiculous for anyone who has handled (as most ancients had, and as few moderns have) real birds. When you next see a dead sparrow or blackbird at the roadside, pick it up. Its fragility will appal you. If you know about the violence of the wind and the sea (as most ancients did, and few moderns do), the idea that a willow warbler or a swift might battle across the wine-dark sea seems not just fanciful but sacrilegious. It took Odysseus, the man of many tricks, adept with a sword and javelin, ten years to get from Troy to Ithaca. If Poseidon punished his presumption so savagely, what would he do with a little bundle of fluff? Remember what he did that disastrous April in the Aegean?

Even Aristotle, a superb natural historian, a keen observer, and a man relatively unencumbered by presumption, thought (though he acknowledged the possibility of migration) that it was at best unusual. Garden warblers, he held, change into blackcaps, and redstarts into robins in winter. And many birds just stayed.

> Many of the birds too [ie as well as fish] hide; it
> is not, as some people think, that only a few do,
> or that all of them migrate to warm places. Some
> birds, including kites and swallows, withdraw to
> such places if their ordinary residence is nearby;
> but those that live further away from such places
> do not migrate, but conceal themselves. For in
> the past many swallows have been seen in holes,
> stripped of all their feathers, and kites have been
> seen flying out of such places when they make
> their first appearance …

Aristotle's natural history was so unimpeachable in antiquity, and became so canonical in the Middle Ages, that these ideas, bolstered by some unlikely and constantly recycled reports of swallows hibernating under water, died hard. They began to be eroded from the seventeenth century, but the erosion was slow. Samuel Johnson, who never had any doubts about anything, had no doubts about this: 'Swallows certainly sleep all winter. A number of them conglobulate together, by flying round and round, and then all in a heap throw themselves under water and lie in the bed of a river.'

Gilbert White, the great chronicler of arrivals and departures, hedged his bets: '… [T]hough most of the swallow kind [in which he included swifts] may yet migrate … some do stay behind and hide with us during the winter.' And so did the anatomist, John Hunter:

> If swallows sleep in the winter, as it is said, it must
> be very different from the manner in which the bear,
> dormouse, lizards, snakes, etc do. Some of these
> really sleep most of the time; the others are in a state
> of stupor or insensibility: but the swallow must be
> in a state of total suspense of animal action, such as
> they say people are when in a trance. There can be
> no circulation, as there can be no respiration.

Hunter conducted experiments that suggested that swallows didn't hibernate under water. He caught swallows, put them into a room with a large tub of water, and left them. All but one died, and not one chose to hibernate in the tub.

It was left to Edward Jenner to perform the brutally definitive experiment. 'I have taken a swift about the 10th of August, which may be considered the eve of its departure, and plunged it into water; but like the generality of animals which respire atmospheric air, it was dead in two minutes.'

That one drowned bird seemed to conclude a debate that had raged for the last two and a half thousand years, and yet Jenner thought that *metaphysical* reasons were almost as conclusive. He noted that at the time the swifts disappear, the world is warm and wonderful, and there is lots of food. 'At such a time', he writes, 'what can be the inducement to them and their young ones, which have just begun to enjoy the motions of their wings and play among the sunbeams to take this dreary plunge.' These are creatures of light and life, he was saying. It's unthinkable that they'd choose darkness and temporary death. It would be contrary to the natural order.

I sympathise with the ancients. Swifts often hunt low over water in August. And then they're gone. What more natural than to think that they tilted their tails, angled down a fraction, and nestled between the reeds at the bottom of the pond. The swifts might have denied themselves the remaining light of the summer, but it would help a chilly, benighted European to know, on a dreary February day, that the embodiment of summer was still here somewhere.

Perhaps that was Aristotle's real agenda. Perhaps he was writing not science, but another resurrection myth along the lines of the story of Persephone and Demeter. Look out over the most dismal place – the frozen lake. Beneath it, crystallised in a bird's body, is the summer, and soon the bird will burst out of the dark, screech victory, circle up to the sun and, next winter, bring the sun down into the mud so that nowhere is ever really dark and nothing is ever really dead.

Back in Oxford, September doesn't seem like that. It seems that the swifts have taken the sun back to Africa with them, along with warmth and significance.

I'm sitting in my study. There's no companionable scratching of swift chicks. Nothing is darting up impossibly fast, and yet not smashing its feet. The only things screaming down the road are police cars – though they'll be joined in October by drunk students. It's grey, cloudless and cold.

Robert Macfarlane, describing the sharp, smooth turning of swifts, says that it seemed that:

> the air must be honeycombed with transparent
> tubes down which the swifts were sliding, for surely
> nothing else could account for the compressed
> control of their turns. Their flight paths lent contour
> to the sky and their routes the berms and valleys of
> wind which formed and re-formed at that height,
> so that the air appeared to possess a topology of its
> own, made visible by the birds' motion.

Yes! Or rather 'Yes', for this is nothing to be happy about. It means that once they're gone, the sky has no form, no structure. Its beams have been removed and exported to Africa.

One of the most ubiquitous of atavistic fears, appearing in myth after myth, is that the sky will collapse in on us. The absence of the swifts makes that much more likely.

'I'm not worried about the dome of the heavens crashing in', said a friend. 'But I do miss the smell.'

I had no idea what he meant, but then he's a very olfactory animal, who can tell you not just which vineyard and which year a particular Burgundy came from, but what the grape-pickers had for breakfast the week before.

Swifts, he insists, smell like stale Balkan Sobranie tobacco. He says that when they're careering down the street on a still day they leave a vapour trail that makes him sneeze or, on a bad day, gag.

I assumed this was a pose. Nothing of the sort had ever been mentioned to me even by swift-ringers and swift-rehabilitators. And then I stumbled across Henry Douglas-Home's account of his love affair with swifts. It started when he was a boy at Eton. In the summer, after prayers and before lights out, he would lean on his windowsill, smoking an old pipe of his father's and watching the swifts weaving in and out of the fives courts. In their excitement the swifts, he wrote, sometimes overshot and were forced 'to brush past me at my window, leaving a musty aroma on the air which luckily exactly matched my John Cotton No. 1 mixture tobacco.' Sometimes his housemaster, hoping to catch him in some misdemeanour, came in, sniffing suspiciously. Douglas-Home would explain that he was 'just watching these lovely swifts. Beautiful the way they circle around screaming.' 'Weally?' queried the housemaster, who spoke Ancient Greek without any 'r's' at all. More was needed. 'They have this odd smell, sir. Musty', said Douglas-Home, hopefully. It worked. 'Hm. Yes, I see what you mean. Smells wather like tobacco, doesn't it?' 'I suppose it does, sir. Never thought of it like that.' And the pair would hang convivially out of the window watching the swifts, the pipe burning a hole in Douglas-Home's pocket, before the housemaster slouched off in his flapping slippers, declaring 'Intwiguing birds, intwiguing', leaving Douglas-Home to say goodnight to the swifts and to have a final smoke before bed.

In the Aegean it's a reprise of April. Big seas are running. Waves are rearing over the walls and flooding the fish tavernas. Gulls are driven up into the mountains. A Cory's shearwater is impaled on an olive branch in the Taygetus.

A bridled tern twitches upside down in a cypress tree on Kythera. And a group of migrating swifts from Bucharest, expecting to be over Libya now, encrust an old lighthouse on a foam-flecked rock off Crete, crammed onto ledges, burrowing into the damp mass of other birds to escape the fury, the salt starting to frost their faces, their eyes tight shut, their metabolism trying to remember the times when they were nestlings and the weather and the flies failed, and they shut down harmlessly for a week and came alive when the sun came back.

This time their physiology isn't so forgiving. In the morning the foam on the rock is black with chewed feathers.

The Caspian Sea is dead-black and mirror-flat, but if you were staring quietly into the water from a boat on the eastern edge you might see in the mirror, for a moment, the tremor of things even blacker than the water. They are *Apus apus pekinensis,* the Asian subspecies of the common swift, and all in this group of thirty birds bred within a few feet of one another in the gilded splendour of one of the old Imperial palaces of Beijing. So far as their accommodation goes, they're some of the most secure swifts in the world, for they are the spirits of dead ancestors, and to block up one of their holes would be to kick your grandfather onto the street.

Tonight they will feast in the foothills of Mount Ararat, and then play for a few days with the headwaters of the Tigris and Euphrates before flying over Damascus, down the Jordan valley, over the Red Sea, and up the Nile.

★

Some Danish swifts, fresh from a bracing Baltic archipelago, linger in the Ardèche. They met there, but treated with disdain, Dutch birds hatched in an old canal-side house that had seen horrific things. When the Danes and the Dutch move on to the Pyrenees, they take the same route – perhaps following a map etched into their heads since the last ice age – but a day apart.

Czech birds, several of them spewed out of the mouths of gothic gargoyles, decide to stay for a while on a brown plain in central Spain. It is not clear why.

But most common swifts are in Africa by now. The Sahel is lighting up with shimmering black lights coming from the north. The Mediterranean was unkind to these birds this time. It was not only that Aegean rock that macerated them. Broken swift bodies are washed up amongst the beach umbrellas in Tunisia, the merry little boats of Algiers, and along the empty pale strands of Libya that rise gently to become the Sahara.

This was an unusually bad year for swifts. An astonishing proportion of them usually survive. Amongst the survivors in the Sahel there's a feeling of muted fiesta. Some of the summer's close relationships have been smashed by the sea, and the desert picked off some of the ocean-battered ones: they lost height and dropped slowly into the baking plains. Their efforts to rise became twitches, and then those stopped.

The sun burns off the worst memories. A tight cluster

of birds that travelled together from an Oslo housing estate whirr around an acacia, more like swallows than swifts, drunk on the heat. Unlike Monty Python's Norwegian Blue parrot, they're plainly not pining at all for the fjords.

Some will stay here for the winter. Why wouldn't they? There's a reasonable living to be made. The camels and the donkeys kick flies out of the rough grass. But most, after a bit of reacclimatisation, re-learning the dialects of the insects and the accents of the winds, carry on south.

approach
towards nest box

'basking' towards eaves

flying up
to nest box

'falling away from eaves'

dropping away from eaves
tail pressed down

July 12th   swifts prospecting   9.15am. Up to five birds
landing on occupied nest box and landing on other nest boxes occasionally

October

Not all of them, though.

I've taken to scanning the literature for accounts of late-leaving swifts. It's pathetic – like a doomed man writing round for all the quack remedies he can find. There's always been a ready market for fake news about over-wintering swifts, whether they're hibernating in the mud at the bottom of every other pond or lying torpid but alive in Longnor Chapel in Shropshire in February 1766 – as Thomas Pennant reported. And though swifts are very rare in Europe after mid-September, there are always occasional birds around for a while after that to stoke ridiculous hopes that after all, and despite the gloom, smog and freezing rain, we live somewhere they choose to stay.

There's a heart-warming, winter-mitigating report from a village in the high mountains of south-western Bulgaria. On October 4 common swifts were seen looping up into cracks between the gutter and the eaves of two buildings, one in a tiny village, the other standing alone in a meadow. Intrigued, the investigators went closer, and heard the cheeping of nestlings. It wasn't all that warm. During the day the temperature in the meadow was around 12 degrees centigrade; at night it fell to 1 degree.

In a mountain monastery nearby, pallid swifts were found to be nesting too, and young were heard begging for food on November 3, though the air temperature was between 6 and 9 degrees. The doughty biologists scooped up dung samples from under the pallid swift nest sites. *Hymenoptera* were the main food. There was only one beetle and one true bug.

It had been an unusually rainy summer in the Bulgarian mountains. Perhaps the swifts had put off breeding in the hope that things would get better and at last, desperate, decided to stake everything on the ants, wasps and bees of the beech woods, pine forests and fields. I hope it worked out for them. The report, frustratingly, doesn't say whether these nestlings ever flew the nest.

The entanglement of one species with another is one of the abiding joys and mysteries: humans with dogs and cats; the hippo, Owen, and the Aldabra Giant Tortoise, Mzee, inseparable in a Kenya animal sanctuary; the Indian leopard that slipped every night into a village to sleep curled up with a calf; a lioness mothering an oryx; Gavin Maxwell and Henry Williamson with their otters; dolphins with the shipwrecked sailors they nudge or carry to shore; the sperm whales who adopted a bottlenose dolphin with a spinal deformity.

The reason for some of these associations is plain enough. Sometimes it's a case of multiplying the number of sensory receptors, to the benefit of everyone except the predator. Thus short-sighted but keen-eared zebras team up with eagle-eyed giraffe and wildebeest on the savanna.

Sometimes one species is better than another at locating a particular type of food which can then be exploited by the other – and so having many food-finding skills in a flock is good for all. But often there is no obvious advantage – and that is particularly true for some bird flocks. When fieldfares and redwings come to Britain from Scandinavia in the winter, it's usual to find them together. They're both thrushes; they doubtless share the same basic skills. And it's not that they're found in the same fields because they want the same food – though they do. They fly as one; a redwing is as likely to be shoulder to shoulder with a fieldfare as with a redwing.

It's like that with common swifts and pallid swifts, as that Bulgarian report showed. To us they look and sound very similar, and I've already confessed that, so desperate am I to see common swifts, I don't look too closely for fear of seeing a rather larger, more distinct throat patch, or primary feathers that look blacker than the rest of the forewing. Common swifts, says the authoritative text, appear 'structurally more rakish'. To me, rakishness is a more obvious characteristic than the uniformity of the outer primary coverts and the surrounding coverts. Their flight, the text goes on, 'can appear more dashing and agile.' Rakishness, dashingness and agility are in the eye of the beholder, and if I want to see them, you just try to stop me.

If I had the honesty and ability to look closely at groups of biggish dark swifts in southern Europe and Africa, I think there would be a fair chance of seeing common swifts and pallid swifts together.

For many years I'd go often to Aswan, in Upper Egypt. And there I'd sit by the side of the Nile, drinking hibiscus tea, eating *fuul*, watching the sun stalk round Elephantine Island, and telling myself that each stick that floated past might have been spat out by a hippo in Lake Victoria.

One late October morning, an embattled refugee from the taunting swiftlessness of England, I walked down to the Nile shore to start the day's vigil. There, catching flying ants whose ancestors might have mopped up the blood of sacrificial bulls or eaten the brains of pharaohs, were some very familiar black birds. Leaning against a palm tree, slapping venomous flies and pouring water over my head at noon, I watched them for eight hours until they moved on upstream into Nubia.

I learned a lot that day. I saw, for instance, that swifts fly by falling perpetually forwards; that they are fast gliders, but can't go far without losing height and needing to shiver their wings (what in other birds would be flapping). But, most usefully, I learned that there were limits even to my well-trained capacity for comforting delusion.

These, I'd insisted to myself, were common swifts, which might have come from Tuscany or the Peloponnese – both of which I was missing badly – and I had a homely glow of the kind that you get when you bump into an old friend in a distant place.

It didn't survive lunch. Part of me knew that common swifts aren't to be found here – at least at this time of year – and that part slowly wore down the rest of me until, by lunchtime, I was forced to give in. These were pallid swifts, I was all on my own, two and a half thousand miles from home, and the universe had just played a nasty, malicious trick on me.

I sat in the bar in the Old Cataract hotel that night, fulminating into red wine, before slinking back to my doss house round the corner, where I despondently squashed bed bugs until dawn.

Years later I learned that some common swifts might overwinter in Africa, and indeed that they might be found amongst flocks of pallid swifts along the Nile. It was a redemptive read. I need not have fumed that night.

What are *Apus apus* and *Apus pallidus* doing together? Do they like one another's company because they want a change from their own kind – just as all sane Brits prefer curry to pie and peas, and Cairo to Cleethorpes? Does the (presumably) musty smell of the other have an exotic allure? Is the real agenda genetic? Is natural selection whispering in their feathered ears: 'Hybrid vigour is powerful. Hybrids are safe repositories for your genes. Species boundaries are illusory. Try it on'?

The October swifts are starting to look dog-eared. Having arrived in Africa, they've started their main moult. They are shedding Europe. The fibreglass-contaminated feathers that sprouted in our road are now forced out like milk teeth and woven into the nests of mice and mousebirds. The feathers, like Europe itself, have done their job. Now is a relatively undemanding time, when the swifts can afford to be slightly less tight on the turn than in the summer; when, if they're tired, they can roost in the updraught behind a storm.

If you want to follow swifts around Africa, the rule is *follow the green.* And that means following the rain. Insect numbers peak four to six weeks after the start of the rains. So you should track the march of the ITCZ – the Inter-Tropical

Convergence Zone (which is where the north-east and south-east trade winds smash into one another), and follow a month behind. You'll find yourself in a feeding frenzy – of swarming termites in particular.

I've not done it systematically. It's not a comfortable time to be in Africa. It's peak mosquito time, and even if you escape malaria, yellow fever, Zika, Chikungunya and Dengue, you probably won't get much sleep because there's a hundred-per-cent humidity and it's hot as hell, and you won't get to the good swift sites because the road will have been washed away.

I've intercepted the swifts in a number of places in north, south, east and west Africa. Sometimes I've not been far from where the ITCZ has crackled, grumbled and coiled in to bite its own tail; where the wind is heavy and the clouds sickly; where black columns of insects rise from the bush like the pillars of a Satanic temple.

Once, when I asked in a South African village about swifts, I was told gleefully that they eat them in pies. I didn't believe it. They just wanted to enjoy my outrage. But they might just have been telling the truth. We are the great undiscriminating belly of the world.

Swift nestlings are supposed to be splendid eating, and in Tuscany, at least until the end of the nineteenth century, special swift towers were built, or existing towers or houses adapted to farm swifts for the table. The important thing was to be able to reach in and grab the young. The swift-farmers were careful not to destroy their own business, and left one nestling alive.

The innovative taxidermist and naturalist Charles Waterton, who joined the parts of different animals together to make chimaeras, who moulded the buttocks of a monkey into the shape of his political enemy, and who could scratch the back of his head with his big toe, noted, on his visit to Rome in 1817, that boys caught swifts and house martins with an alluring feather tied to a silk noose, and sold the corpses for food.

The flesh of adult swifts is supposed to be tough. It doesn't surprise me. They have the most strenuous lives on the planet. I've never eaten swifts myself, but I was once snowed into a village in the Greek mountains, and had nothing to eat for a week but small songbirds and chips. It was not only shameful but unpleasant – like eating rubber marinated in chicken stock.

If something can be killed, we kill it, whether or not it can be eaten.

When the temperature suddenly fell in Kent in 1856, swifts, paralysed by the cold, fell out of the sky and tottered drunkenly around. A zoologist from the British Museum happened to be there. A girl, who had heard that he bought all sorts of animals, knocked on his door, asking him if he wanted to buy a bat. The 'bat' was a swift. The church was covered with bats, said the girl, and the boys (of course) were killing them. The zoologist hurried out: 'True enough', he wrote, 'the children were charging them everywhere.' When he got to the church he was astonished to see the birds 'hanging in clusters from the eaves and cornices; some were at least two feet in length, and at intervals benumbed individuals dropped from the outside of the clusters. Many hundreds of the poor birds fell victims to the ruthless ignorance of the poor children.'

Kent was a dangerous place for nineteenth-century swifts. In 1835 strong cold winds forced swifts to hunt low along the streets of Dover, where boys (again) killed them in huge numbers with sticks.

No doubt this goes on all over the world. It tells us a good deal about ourselves, but it's irrelevant to swift conservation. What's killing the swifts is our mania for architectural tidiness; our hatred of crannies, cracks and generally the characterful and the ramshackle; industrial farming, with its sterile, chemical-doused monocultural boringness; and the attitude expressed in a chilling article that made me speechlessly angry for a week. It's ominously entitled *Population of Common Swift in Poznan (Poland) and Ecosystem Services Provided by it*. Read that title again, and weep.

The premise is that the continued existence of swifts needs to be justified economically – because, naturally, there is no other possible type of justification. The most important 'ecosystem services' provided by birds in cities, we're told, are 'regulating and cultural services'. The 'most noticeable regulating service is pest control'. How do swifts help? By catching insects. The author cites studies saying that each day a pair of swifts takes an average of 20,000 flying insects, weighing 50 grammes, back to their growing nestlings, and went on to calculate that the estimated actual population of swifts in Poznan should eat, each season, 4.04 million flying insects, weighing a total of 0.4 tonnes. If, as he presumes, swifts in Poznan had declined by 86 per cent in the last half century, that means that there are 2.9 tonnes of insects flying over Poznan that, with a healthy swift population, would not be. 'Flying insects … if not … eaten by swifts could be [a] nuisance for inhabitants of cities (eg by biting) and also negatively affect plants (eg by feeding on them).' The uncaught insects represent 'a significant amount of lost benefits in reduction of [the] bothersome insect population.'

And the 'cultural services'? Well, birds 'are often one of a few possibilities for people living in the cities to experience contact with nature. Most … birds except species like pigeons and aquatic birds are usually difficult to spot, but sounds of birds can be heard almost everywhere in cities … '. The author, however, seems not to rate swifts high as cultural-service providers: 'Studies on residents of residential blocks in Rzeszow', he gloomily notes, 'showed that despite these ecosystem services, only [a] small group (12 per cent) of people notice [the] impact of birds on improving the welfare of themselves.'

I'm sure the author means well; that he's a genuine nature-lover. But if we agree to play the neoliberal game –the game whose rule is that everything has a value that can be stated in dollars – we're finished. The presumption that swifts need to justify themselves in terms that mean something to us is malignant and highly metastatic. Who are we to demand that the wild world pleads for its life in language that we can understand? If we set ourselves up as judges of what has a right to exist, we are saying that we are gods, with unlimited jurisdiction. If there are to be human judges, should they be bankers rather than poets? How does one audit existence, let alone exuberance or epiphany?

The swifts from the Western Wall shudder in the maritime cold of Angola – an unusual, unseasonal cold welling up from deep in the south Atlantic. They've arrived rather early. They should have stayed in the Congo until the Angolan rains cracked open the chrysalises and made the ground breathe out the nymphs.

I shudder in the wholly predictable cold of England – a seasonal cold that doesn't well up, but sucks all the heat and life out of everything here. I petulantly spin the globe in the kitchen, and check the prices of flights to central Africa.

November

The eastern swifts, *Apus apus pekinensis,* which are the spirits of dead ancestors, winter mainly in Namibia and Botswana after their long journey. That means that the Chinese are without their dead for the whole of the winter. This seems strange to me; that's when I need my dead most.

Last night a German hunter on a Namibian farm, relaxing after shooting a kudu, knocked out his pipe against a whistling thorn as he waited for the pick-up to collect the body. The smouldering ash fell on a patch of dry earth under the tree, and there was no fire to see by the time the hunter was borne triumphantly off for his celebratory dinner. But in the night the breeze from the waving tail of a passing ground squirrel wafted it into the grass, and by the time the hunter was eating his vast carnivorous breakfast, fire had begun to crawl.

At first the crawl was slow; it had been a windless night. But a gentle wind came up with the sun, and the fire ran before it, and before the fire ran Cape hares, jackals, elephant shrews, dik-dik and duiker; and before it slithered cobras and sand snakes; and legions of scorpions too, tails raised impotently to sting the fire back.

The smoke was as blue as a fine July sky in Oxfordshire, and swimming through it were hundreds of dead Chinese. Their foreheads – which look like snowploughs, and which had just ploughed through the cloud from Mongolia – were paler than those of the European swifts, but otherwise they looked identical to me. They spun, they somersaulted, they fluffed up their feathers, they shivered with what looked like intense pleasure, they burrowed to the heart of the smoke, so near to the crackling grass that I expected them to rise as balls of flame and seed other fires when they finally fell. This was high-energy luxuriating: lots of wriggling and tail-spreading. I wonder if they held their breath.

Nobody really knows why birds do this smoke-bathing. It's been recorded in several species. Typically a bird stands on the top of a smoking chimney with outspread wings and the type of drugged, beatific expression you see on the faces of birds when they squat on the ground, letting formic-acid-squirting ants run over them. The similar posture, along with the absence of any other ideas, makes people assume that smoke-bathing is, like anting, for the control of ectoparasites like fleas and lice.

I have a problem with that sort of mechanistic language. Does the bird think it's *for* parasite control? Or does it think it's for the pleasure it undoubtedly gives? I'd opt for the pleasure every time. If that's right, then what's the 'real' reason? Is pleasure just the bait that natural selection sticks on the hook in order to get an organism to behave in a way that gives it a selective advantage? Are pleasure and joy incidental by-products of behaviour actually driven by some deeper motor, inaudible and impalpable to ordinary consciousness?

This sounds like a vain and pedantic inquiry. It certainly has no incontestably right answer. Perhaps this just illustrates the meaninglessness of fundamental 'Why?' type questions. That's what my reductionist ex-friend – the brilliant biologist – would say. But I'd point out to him that biologists spend their whole working lives asking and answering 'Why?' questions. Why do Manx Shearwaters go *there* rather than *there*? Why does a hedgehog's prickle have the tensile strength it does? Why fly from Namibia to Ulan Bataar and back? Why did the chicken cross the road?

The answers can be given at various levels, but the biologists' most fundamental answer to all these questions – just like the answer to the old joke about the chicken – is always the same: to increase the number of offspring it is likely to produce in its lifetime. Success as a biologist is (far too often) not about finding the answer to the question posed; that is known before anyone starts work. It's about squeezing the answer neatly into the canonical paradigm.

But there's a far more difficult, mysterious and worthwhile 'Why?' question. Why bother?

Why bother to bring more bodies into the world to labour away on the same onerous reproductive project? Is it that the organism fears personal extinction and sees its only hope of immortality in the persistence of its genes beyond the grave? If it's not that, what is it? Who or what is behind the great lust for living? Natural selection seems too weak, on its own, to propel the whole of the biological world at the pace and with the passion it has.

Perhaps sucking the sweetness of relationship – even if it's biologically barren – is a reason for bothering? Perhaps the joy of punching head-first through a big wave is a reason for bothering – even if the cold depresses your libido and makes you less likely to impregnate your partner with the currently loaded sperm? Perhaps the spa- or nail-bar-type pleasure of flying through the smoke of a Namibian bush-fire is a reason for bothering?

Urgent shouts from the direction of the farm jolted me out of this meditation. The fire was moving towards me. Yes, but not fast. It was an unimpressive little fire, flaring up for a moment when a new block of air shunted the old one out of the way, but mostly wicking on like water in a towel.

I walked back over the blackened ground, which was still warm. I'd known a few bush fires, including some that had overhauled even big, fast runners. Here, though, the bodies were of small, slow things: charcoal snakes and small mammals singed bald. But though the fire wasn't dramatic, there was no getting away from it: the swifts had been luxuriating in the smoke of a crematorium.

They'd got out of the bath now, and were killing the panicking insects rising from the far fringe of the fire. These birds may kill flies from the dung of Cape fur seals at the grunting colonies on the coast, follow the herds of zebra galloping through the water of the Okavango Delta, or play in the rainbow spray of thundering falls on the Zambezi before taking the Silk Road back to the ancestral temples of Imperial China. When you talk about swifts you become an insufferable romantic just by spelling out the facts.

These, as I said, are the Asian subspecies of the common swift. The birds we met in Jerusalem (and which are probably now in Angola, Zambia or the DRC) are thought to be intermediate between *Apus apus* and *Apus apus pekinensis*.

Over the years aggressive taxonomists have tried to draw

me into their fights about swift classification, and genial, musing taxonomists have tried to interest me in the issues. They've both failed.

Here's a flavour of the conversation:

'Recent molecular phylogeny placed this species [*Apus apus*] in a clade with *A. niansae*, *A. bradfieldi*, *A. barbatus*, *A. berliozi*, *A. unicolor*, *A. alexandri* and *A. pallidus*. Previously thought to be closest to *A. niansae* and *A. unicolor*; has been considered conspecific with both, and also with *A. barbatus*. Birds breeding in south-west Asia have been separated as race *marwitzi*, but this poorly differentiated taxon not widely accepted. Israeli population somewhat intermediate between nominate race and *pekinensis*. Two subspecies normally recognised.'

I don't cite this to mock or parody. I'm in respectful awe. This kind of meticulous science has told us so much about the genealogy of species – where they've come from. It's fascinating and important family history. My quarrel is simply that it is family *history:* not family *present* or family *future.* Though it presumes the past fluidity of species, it doesn't acknowledge the present fluidity of species. It pretends that you can point to a bird and say, without any doubt: 'That is *Apus apus pekinensis.*' And we can't. In a couple of million years' time – a blink in evolution's eye – there won't be such a subspecies. And there isn't really such a subspecies now. It only exists as a category in the minds of its advocates.

Darwin's great insight was that species are mutable, but that's sometimes forgotten. We're more attached to our categories (because *we* made them) than to the reality of the natural world. You can't point to a bird and say 'That's a common swift', any more than you can point to a place in a river and say 'That point, just there, is the Nile.' Everything is *process:* everything is flux.

The flux will sweep away all our cherished pigeon-holes. I've never seen a common swift. Never will. There's no such thing. But I have seen lots and lots of individual, fast, heart-stopping birds, each of them with individual tastes and orientations, each with a completely different story.

That's it! Story. We're all intimately interrelating stories, each with a part in every other story.

Stories were bathing in the smoke of other stories; were snatching, squashing, and recycling the life of other stories; drawing some stories to a close so that they could carry on telling their own.

This is all very fine, but it doesn't help when the dark closes in. It gives no comfort beside our parents' graves.

We might say, too, that ecosystems were bathing in the smoke of other ecosystems, and recycling those other ecosystems. I'm an ecosystem too. Kill the bacteria and fungi that fill and coat me, and I'll die. Rip me out of the nexus of relationships with humans and non-humans that I call my life and I'll stop being me. Not only is the idea of a species meaningless, but the idea of an individual is problematic. I can't tell you where the species *Apus apus* starts and stops, and I can't tell you what that conspicuously aeronautical individual over that small herd of springbok is.

If we sequenced its DNA we'd be able to tell that it was a member of the common swift species – which really means that it had a lot of base pairs in common with other birds that we have decided to call 'common swifts'. That DNA is in each of its cells, but the bird is a lot more than those cells. Not only is 'it' the community of its cells, its protozoa, fungi and other microorganisms, but 'it' is also its history, its memories and its tendencies. Stories again. 'It' is stories nesting inside stories inside stories inside stories: it's a Russian doll that happened to hatch in China. The swift looks so neat and discrete, but there's no way of saying where its boundaries are; no way of saying where it, or I, or anything else begins or ends.

None of this helps in the dark or in cemeteries either.

It's true that everything is change; everything's a flowing stream. But swifts, as the name 'swift' suggests, flow faster than others. They live harder; they pack more in. And their habits change fast too. Before humans had houses, swifts had nests, and now swifts nest more or less only in human buildings.

It may be that the calendar of common swift migration is changing. The evidence is equivocal – though there is a suggestion that they may be arriving slightly earlier than before, particularly in sunnier southern Europe, and possibly in Eurasia, but they departed significantly earlier from the UK in the 2000s compared to the 1960s. Probably more of them are wintering north of the Sahara than just a few years ago. And there is clear evidence that climate change is increasing their range in South Africa. There, as elsewhere, the swifts follow the insects. In a hotter climate, insects reach adulthood earlier; there are more insect generations for the birds to harvest.

There's lots of gloom about the future of swifts. I suspect they have a brighter future than us. When *Homo sapiens* has gone there will be lots of ideal swift holes in the decaying buildings we'll leave behind.

★

The name *Apus apus* comes from the Greek *A pus* – no feet – on account of swifts' usually invisible feet.

Humans use their feet for moving, but flying birds use them for staying still: for perching and for standing. Feet, for a flying bird, are an acknowledgment of inadequacy. They show that the bird hasn't colonised the air fully, isn't thoroughly at home there.

Swifts' feet are a badge of aeronautical prowess. When they land, it's usually just at the nesting site, and there their feet are more like the wheels on the undercarriage of a landing aircraft than like normal, grasping feet.

No animal migrant could walk from south-west Africa to east Asia in spring, breed, and be back in autumn. The land would defeat it. The miles would eat it. Swifts know more of the land than terrestrial creatures because they are extra-terrestrial, and footless to prove it.

So it is extra-terrestrial narrative ecosystems, of indeterminate species, who have no clear beginning, no clear end and no clear borders, but who are said to be dead Chinese, and who may have inspired the idea of the Cherubim, who are scooping and twisting in the late-afternoon smoke, and preparing to spend the night tucked up in a cloud before moving off – for they've smelt a rumour of rain a couple of hundred miles north.

'They're bloody birds, for Christ's sake', says the ex-friend.

Well, exactly.

December

It's just after dawn. I'm crouched in the wood near our house in Oxford. Rain is falling fitfully – whenever the sky can be bothered. But mostly it can't. It's too tired. There's no wind. Nothing's moving except the occasional clattering wood pigeon, my old friend the fox (and he moves so softly that the movement is more like growth than ordinary animal motion), and the cold, which crawls out of the ground and winds itself round my legs and my kidneys.

The fox has the only colour. There's certainly none in me.

The sky is flat. It might be an inch in front of my nose or a million miles away; there's no telling. Even the pigeons don't want to fly through it; they just reel from branch to branch. They seem to think that a sky like this won't support them.

I'm not surprised. It doesn't have any texture, any infrastructure; any of the tubes through which Robert Macfarlane's swifts slide. It might fall in at any moment.

It's five months since the swifts were rocketing through the arch made by those sycamore branches, curling back, and rolling over like crocodiles to grab and shake the big hoverflies drawn up from the blackberries.

It's no use pretending I'm dealing with this well. It's no use saying that the wood and the world are not worse in December, but just *different*. It's no use reminding myself that the geese are here, that if I drove for a bit I could see huge flocks of waders spinning over the Severn estuary, or that the fulmars have already returned to the nest sites in north Devon that I've mapped. It's no use repeating to myself that this is the same sky through which swifts are slicing in Zambia.

It does help, sometimes, to know that the swifts are there somewhere, in places that I know. It sometimes helps to put on recordings of their screams, to cross off the number of days left until May like a homesick boarding-school kid, or to follow the news from the Congo.

But having erotic thoughts is not the same as having sexual intercourse.

I uncoiled, stretched and marched lustfully home to book a flight.

I waited for them. I drank lots more Laurentina beer. I got a faceful of halitotic sea spray from a southern right whale. I went out to the island to say hello to the dead slave trader. I clambered up the ridge every night to look into the interior of Mozambique. I went to the internet café to check the weather and the ornithological blogs. I threw lumps of gristle to the dogs. I sweated, darned the holes in my mosquito net and watched olive bee-eaters taking food to their young in a long burrow. I emailed home, saying 'What on earth am I doing here?', and felt guilty about leaving the family on yet another trip. I lay awake, listening to hyenas cackling and the damp slap of bat wings. I sat under an umbrella and saw the rain bounce and carve a new channel through the yard which would let it get back sooner to the sea. I watched giraffe sway between the baobabs, and the palms bend to the wind from the ocean. I sat in the footprint of a beach elephant and saw the sky pucker, swell and burst. I saw monkeys pulling ticks from their friends' anuses and crushing them with stones. I finished *Great Expectations* and moved on to *Nicholas Nickleby*.

They did not come.

I found a fish box from Jakarta, a beer can from Cairo, a monogrammed plate from a luxury cruise ship based in Florida, a turtle's flipper, a booby's beak and the aborted foetus of a porpoise.

And still they did not come.

I know how it is, I thought. They're somewhere in Malawi, eating termites. If I book my ticket back, that'll flush them out. They'll stoop low over me just as I'm boarding the plane.

I boarded the plane. The sky was empty.

It is easier now to bear the flat Oxford sky. They chose not to be here, just as they chose not to be in Mozambique. I would not want it to be different. When a will like theirs is loose in the world, it wouldn't be right to rein it in; to make it a suburb of my own will.

I said that although they're called common swifts, they're the least common thing. That was wrong. Their power, freedom and joy are the way that everything really is – though we don't usually see it. It is just that when the swifts scream through the sky, you can't miss it. That's how everything, all the time, is meant to be.

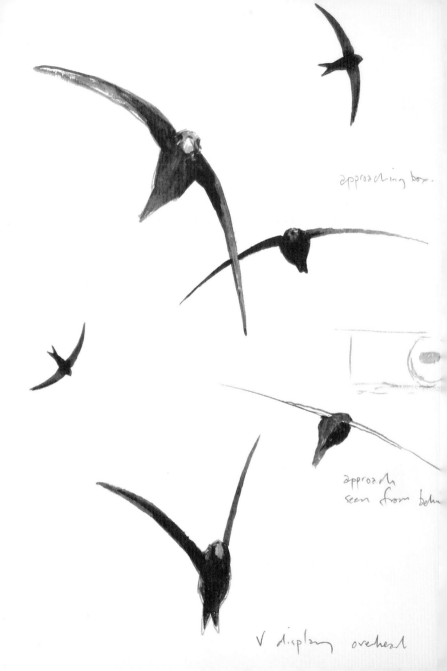

approaching box.

approach
seen from below

V display overhead

References

p. 7 'There are thought to be about 18,000 bird species on the planet'
www.amnh.org

p. 15 'Non-breeding swifts don't land, most of them sometimes do'
Anders Hedenström, Gabriel Norevik, Kajsa Warfvinge,
Arne Andersson, Johan Bäckman and Susanne Åkesson:
'Annual 10-month aerial life phase in the Common Swift
Apus apus.' *Current Biology* 26(22) (2016), 3066–3070.

p. 17 'It takes them around 26 days'
Based on Susanne Åkesson, Raymond Klaassen, Jan
Holmgren, James W. Fox and Anders Hedenström:
'Migration routes and strategies in a highly aerial migrant, the
Common Swift *Apus apus*, revealed by light-level geolocators.'
PloS one 7(7) (2012): e41195, p. 7, but adjusted to account for
the fact that that paper dealt with Swedish swifts.

p. 18 '3.23 trips to the moon'
The distance to the moon varies, but it is around 238,855
miles away.

p. 18 'trip to the sun'
The sun is around 93 million miles away.

p. 18 'the staples of three-quarters of modern humans'
For a magnificent overview of the facts and politics of food,
see Carolyn Steel: *Sitopia: How Food Can Save the World*,
Random House, 2020.

p. 18 'Swifts prey on around five hundred different species'
Josef Rajchard, Jan Procházka and Pavel Kindlmann: 'Long-
term decline in Common Swift *Apus apus* annual breeding
success may be related to weather conditions.' *Ornis Fennica*
83(2) (2006), 66: Mostly aphids, Hymenoptera, Coleoptera,
and Diptera.

p. 19 'One fifth of all meals in the USA are eaten in a car'
Sitopia, op. cit.

p. 20 Wilfred Owen
'The Swift', in *The complete poems and fragments of Wilfred Owen*, Chatto & Windus, 1983.

p. 20 Janet Andrews
A Day in a Life is Janet's Story, Memoirs Publishing, 2012.

p. 20 'It is the things that ignore us that save us in the end'
Andrew Harvey, *A Journey in Ladakh*, Houghton Mifflin Harcourt, 1983.

p. 22 'And the swift flicked through the breath of a violet'
Ted Hughes, *Crow and the Birds*, in *Crow*, Faber, 1970.

p. 22 Randle Manwaring
The Swifts of Maggiore, Fuller D'Arch Smith Ltd, 1981.

p. 22 Hugh David Loxdale
Swifts, in *Bird Words: Poetic images of wild birds*, Brambleby Books, 2003.

p. 22 'the globe's still working'
Ted Hughes, *Swifts*, in *Season Songs*, Faber, 1975.

p. 23 'On a steep/Controlled scream of skid'
Swifts, ibid.

p. 23 Anne Collie
Swifts at Letcombe, Collie, 1997.

p. 23 'slashing/Rents in summer skies'
Derek Ramsay, *The Return Stick*, no other reference available.

p. 23 'cleaving the still air'
Peter Fish, *Swifts: Superstars*, Fish, 1981.

p. 23 'come to distribute death'
Hugh David Loxdale, *Swifts*, ibid.

p. 23 'For sure they are Satan's cherubim'
Roger Yates, *Swift Summer*, Yates, 2009.

p. 23 'The black depths of their devil thoughts'
Trevor J. James, *Devil Birds*, no other reference available.

p. 24 W. H. Hudson
       Afoot in England, Hutchinson, 1909.

p. 24 John Clare
       Northborough Sonnets, Robinson, Eric (ed), Carcanet, 1995.

p. 24 C. S. Lewis
       A Grief Observed (sub. nom. N. W. Clerk), Faber, 1961.

p. 24 R. S. Thomas
       Swifts, in Collected Poems, 1945–1990, Dent, 1993.

p. 25 Gilbert White
       The Naturalist's Summer Evening Walk, in *The Natural History
       and Antiquities of Selborne, in the County of Southampton. To
       Which are Added, The Naturalist's Calendar; Observations on
       Various Parts of Nature; and Poems*, White, Cochrane, 1813.

p. 27 'there are 95–165 million'
       http://datazone.birdlife.org/species/factsheet/

p. 30 'Swift survival is generally very high'
       Studies on swift mortality are summarised at Giovanni
       Boano, Irene Pellegrino, Mauro Ferri, Marco Cucco, Fausto
       Minelli, and Susanne Åkesson: 'Climate anomalies affect
       annual survival rates of swifts wintering in sub-Saharan
       Africa.' *Ecology and evolution* 10(14) (2020), 7916–7928.

p. 33 'Is there an indefinable style of flying that characterises
       Danish birds, just as the same shirt hangs indescribably
       differently on Danish shoulders?' During the proofing stage
       of this book, a reader thought this was racist. To anyone
       who agrees, I should say that being non-racist doesn't entail
       pretending that the world is a monoculture (it obviously
       and gloriously isn't), or that people everywhere are the
       same (they are splendidly varied), but in discriminating
       on the basis of the differences. This is all trite. It shouldn't
       need to be said. The observation in the text arose from a
       conversation with an Israeli soldier. She said that after a few
       months of duty in the Old City of Jerusalem the soldiers
       know very accurately, on the basis of inchoate clues, the
       nationality of most of the tourists who traipse through the
       streets. Every birdwatcher, relying on the 'jizz' of a bird for

identification, will understand exactly what she meant. Some of those soldiers no doubt use the information they acquire from the clues in order to discriminate. That is racist and evil. It's the use of information that constitutes racism. Facts themselves aren't racist.

p. 34 'Do the other swifts look at them with particular regard'
They don't just fly long distances, they fly very high. They forage to well over 12,000 feet (4000 m) in the Himalayas, and have been known to migrate across Ladakh at 18,500 feet (5700 m). See Cornell Lab of Ornithology: www.birdsoftheworld.org.

p. 34 'the birds of the Near East'
The first swifts in Israel are seen in each year in southern Israel at the end of January. They are at the Western Wall in Jerusalem from mid/end February (Amnonn Hahn: Personal communication).

p. 35 'First World War pilot'
David Lack, *Swifts in a Tower* (revised ed), Unicorn, 2018, p. 128.

p. 36 'manically stocking up glycogen'
In fact birds seem to store relatively little glucose as glycogen. See Eldon J. Braun and Karen L. Sweazea: 'Glucose regulation in birds.' *Comparative Biochemistry and Physiology Part B: Biochemistry and Molecular Biology* 151(1) (2008), 1-9.

p. 38 'The bird became Eocypselus vincenti'
Harrison, C. J. O. 'A revision of the fossil swifts (Vertebrata, Aves, Suborder, Apodi), with descriptions of three new genera and two new species.' *Mededelingen van de Werkgroep voor Tertiaire en Kwartaire Geologie* 21(4) (1984), 157–177.

p. 38 'Eocene Fur Formation'
Mayr, Gerald: 'Reappraisal of Eocypselus – a stem group apodiform from the early Eocene of Northern Europe.' *Palaeobiodiversity and Palaeoenvironments* 90(4) (2010), 395–403. See too Gerald Mayr: 'Skeletal morphology of the middle Eocene swift Scaniacypselus and the evolutionary history of true swifts (Apodidae).' *Journal of Ornithology* 156(2) (2015), 441–450.

p. 39 'Green River Formation'
Daniel T. Ksepka, Julia A. Clarke, Sterling J. Nesbitt, Felicia B. Kulp, and Lance Grande: 'Fossil evidence of wing shape in a stem relative of swifts and hummingbirds (Aves, Pan-Apodiformes).' *Proceedings of the Royal Society B: Biological Sciences*, 280, 1761 (2013): 20130580.

p. 40 'late Eocene extinction'
Probably in two pulses at around 37 and 33 million years ago.

p. 43 Second Temple
It's actually the third. A second temple was built by Zerubbabel, and stood for some five hundred years before Herod's temple replaced it.

p. 43 'Two gigantic golden cherubim'
Kings 6: 23–28.

p. 43 'there I will meet with thee'
Exodus 25:32 (KJV).

p. 44 'Cherubim were carved into the walls and doors'
Kings 6: 23–35.

p. 44 Temple Mount
Other birds nest in the Western Wall too. There are many house sparrows, some jackdaws and some feral pigeons. Some swifts evidently share a nesting hole (or at least the entrance to a nesting hole) with sparrows. See Ulrich Tigges, 'Colony Jerusalem', www.commonswift.org.

p. 45 Amir Balaban
'Migratory swifts put on ancient aerial show at a Western Wall emptied of people', Aviv Lavie, *The Times of Israel*, 12 May 2020.

p. 45 Rabbi Yosef Cornfeld
Common Swift Forum, 24 March 2001: www.commonswift.org.

p. 46 'A day in thy courts'
Psalm 84: 10 (KJV).

p. 47 'Solomon was David's heir'
Sura 27: 15–16.

p. 50 'Liberian fuelling'
Susanne Åkesson, Raymond Klaassen, Jan Holmgren, James W. Fox, and Anders Hedenström: 'Migration routes and strategies in a highly aerial migrant, the Common Swift *Apus apus*, revealed by light-level geolocators.' *PloS one* 7(7) (2012): e41195.

p. 51 'blue-light-sensitive flavoproteins'
See www.ks.uiuc.edu and Thorsten Ritz, Salih Adem and Klaus Schulten: 'A model for photoreceptor-based magnetoreception in birds.' *Biophysical Journal*, 78, 707–718, 2000.

p. 52 'swifts' adjustment of airspeed'
See the discussion in Anders Hedenström and Susanne Åkesson: 'Adaptive airspeed adjustment and compensation for wind drift in the Common Swift: Differences between day and night.' *Animal Behaviour* 127 (2017), 117–123.

p. 54 'tiny GPS systems'
Though at the time of writing no data from GPS devices had been published. It doesn't, apparently, change materially the picture gained from geolocator studies.

p. 54 'whole spring migration'
Akesson et al: 'Migration routes and strategies', op. cit.

p. 54 '"British" swift has been known'
Cited Mike Toms, *Flightlines: Tracking the wonders of bird migration*, British Trust for Ornithology, 2017.

p. 54 'Sweden-bound swifts in spring'
Akesson et al: 'Migration routes and strategies', op. cit.

p. 55 'Five swifts caught soon after arrival'
Akesson et al: 'Migration routes and strategies', op. cit.

p. 57 'visual horizon climbs'
Adriaan M. Dokter, Susanne Åkesson, Hans Beekhuis, Willem Bouten, Luit Buurma, Hans van Gasteren and Iwan Holleman: 'Twilight ascents by Common Swifts, *Apus apus*, at dawn and dusk: acquisition of orientation cues?' *Animal Behaviour* 85(3) (2013), 545–552. See, too, Helen Macdonald: *Vesper Flights*, Jonathan Cape, 2019, pp. 136–144.

p. 57 'That might make a difference'
Meier, Christoph M., Hakan Karaardıç, Raül Aymí, Strahil
G. Peev, Erich Bächler, Roger Weber, Willem Witvliet and
Felix Liechti. 'What makes Alpine swifts ascend at twilight?
Novel geolocators reveal year-round flight behaviour.'
Behavioral Ecology and Sociobiology 72(3) (2018), 45.

p. 58 'the main point of the twilight climbs is *bonding*?'
Cecilia Nilsson, Johan Bäckman and Adriaan M. Dokter:
'Flocking behaviour in the twilight ascents of Common
Swifts *Apus apus*.' *Ibis* 161(3) (2019), 674–678.

p. 66 Boxgrove
C. J. O. Harrison and J. R. Stewart: 'Birds from Boxgrove.'
*The Middle Palaeolithic Site at ARC Eartham Quarry,
Boxgrove, West Sussex, UK* (ed M. B. Roberts and S. A.
Parfitt), *English Heritage Monograph Series* 16, 1990.

p. 66 'UK swift numbers'
The State of the UK's Birds, 2020: www.rspb.org.uk. It is
estimated that in the summer there are 59,000 swifts in the
UK. See also www.bto.org.

p. 66 China
David Lack: *Swifts in a Tower,* op. cit., p. 237.

p. 70 Henry Williamson
'Country commuters flying in the face of danger', in *Days of
Wonder: Contributions to the Daily Express, 1966–1971,* The
Henry Williamson Society, 1987.

p. 73 'extramarital affairs'
Thaís L. F. Martins, Jeremy K. Blakey and Jonathan Wright.
'Low incidence of extra-pair paternity in the colonially
nesting Common Swift *Apus apus*.' *Journal of Avian Biology*
33(4) (2002), 441–446.

p. 74 Carl Safina
Beyond words: What animals think and feel, Macmillan, 2015.

p. 75 Tel Aviv
Ulrich Tigges: 'The spatial and temporal behaviour of a
Common Swift *Apus apus* colony in Tel Aviv.' *Sandgrouse*
25(1) (2003), 49–52.

p. 77 'arrive in and leave Oxford at different times'
Swifts in a Tower, op. cit., p.38.

p. 77 'interesting sperm'
Barrie G. M. Jamieson and Sandro Tripepi: 'Ultrastructure of
the spermatozoon of the Common Swift, with phylogenetic
implications.' *Acta Zoologica* , 86(4) (2005), 239–244.

p. 77 'That opportunity is likely to come'
Swifts in a Tower, op. cit., p. 44.

p. 77 'the female lifted her wings into a 'V'
www.commonswift.org.

p. 78 'much more prone'
Swifts in a Tower, op. cit., p.129.

p. 79 'all fourth nestlings will die'
Sicurella et al: 'Weather conditions, brood size and hatching
order affect Common Swift *Apus apus* nestlings' survival and
growth', ibid.

p. 79 'embryonic development is effectively arrested'
Swifts in a Tower, op. cit., p.76.

p. 83 'more slack in their system'
See the discussion in Beatrice Sicurella, Mario Caffi,
Manuela Caprioli, Diego Rubolini, Nicola Saino and
Roberto Ambrosini: 'Weather conditions, brood size and
hatching order affect Common Swift *Apus apus* nestlings'
survival and growth.' *Bird Study* 62(1) (2015), 64–77.

p. 83 'A young swift, like a young songbird, is hideous'
Swifts in a Tower, op. cit., p. 79.

p. 83 'Their guts are so big'
Swifts in a Tower, op. cit., pp. 80–81.

p.85 'Long-absent swift parents....might have decided to go
hunting in Amsterdam…'
A trip to Amsterdam is in fact unlikely. Breeders probably
stay fairly close to the nest – though non-breeders may travel
huge distances.

p. 85 'sequential hatching'
David Lack: 'The significance of clutch-size.' *Ibis* 89(2) (1947), 302–352, cp Eric Vander Werf. 'Lack's clutch size hypothesis: an examination of the evidence using meta-analysis.' *Ecology* 73(5) (1992), 1699–1705.

p. 86 'parents won't sell themselves short'
Thaís L. F. Martins and Jonathan Wright: 'Brood reduction in response to manipulated brood sizes in the Common Swift (*Apus apus*).' *Behavioral Ecology and Sociobiology* 32(1) (1993), 61–70.

p. 87 'All the survivors, adults and nestlings, benefit'
Thaís L. F. Martins and Jonathan Wright: 'Brood reduction in response to manipulated brood sizes in the Common Swift (*Apus apus*)', ibid.

p. 88 'five per cent of the adult swift's total blood volume'
Mark D. Walker and Ian D. Rotherham: 'The Common Swift louse fly, *Crataerina pallida:* An ideal species for studying host–parasite interactions.' *Journal of Insect Science* 10(1) (2010), 193.

p. 88 'high louse fly loads don't seem to matter'
Mark D. Walker and Ian D. Rotherham: 'The breeding success of Common Swifts *Apus apus* is not correlated with the abundance of their Louse Fly *Crataerina pallida* parasites.' *Bird Study* 57(4) (2010); Mark D. Walker and Ian D. Rotherham: 'Host selection by the Louse Fly *Crataerina pallida*, an avian nest ectoparasite of the Common Swift *Apus apus*.' *Experimental parasitology* 129(1) (2011), 48–54.

p. 89 'The reason for this complex arrangement is obscure'
Cristeta Brause, Hagen Gasse and Gerald Mayr: 'New observations on the splenius capitis and rectus capitis ventralis muscles of the Common Swift *Apus apus* (Apodidae).' *Ibis* 151(4) (2009), 633–639.

p. 91 'They may even build a nest together'
Swifts in a Tower, op. cit., p. 27.

p. 96 'The largest ever daily count of swifts in Britain'
www.birdguides.com.

p. 96 'weather movements'
   Swifts in a Tower, op. cit., pp. 150–151.

p. 100 'a swift enters its nestbox at about 43 miles an hour'
   Anneke van Arkel: 'Dakloze vogels onder dak', *Dakvisie* 04(38) (1997).

p. 100 'a "seemingly impossible" pressure'
   www.commonswift.org

p. 103 'they'll give the children much of the benefit'
   Swifts in a Tower, op. cit., p. 105.

p. 103 'parents eat the nestlings' faecal sacs'
   Giacomo Dell'Omo, Enrico Alleva and Claudio Carere: 'Parental recycling of nestling faeces in the Common Swift.' *Animal Behaviour* 56(3) (1998), 631–637. For discussion of the relative contribution of male and female parents to parenting, see Carere, Claudio and Enrico Alleva. 'Sex differences in parental care in the Common Swift (*Apus apus*): effect of brood size and nestling age.' *Canadian Journal of Zoology* 76(7) (1998), 1382–1387.

p. 104 Surinam
   Marijke N. de Boer, James T. Saulino and Andy C. Williams: 'First documented record of Common Swift *Apus apus* for Surinam and South America.' *Cotinga* 36 (2014), 107–109.

p. 110 'the mathematics of flight'
   Thaís L. F. Martins: 'Fledging in the Common Swift, *Apus apus*: weight-watching with a difference.' *Animal Behaviour* 54(1) (1997), 99–108; Jonathan Wright, Shai Markman and Shaun M. Denney: 'Facultative adjustment of pre-fledging mass loss by nestling swifts preparing for flight.' *Proceedings of the Royal Society B: Biological Sciences* 273: 1596 (2006), 1895–1900.

p. 117 'It used to be thought that it was the light'
   For discussion, see Ulrich Tigges: 'The phenology of the Common Swift *Apus apus* in Eurasia and the problem of defining the duration of their stay.' *Podoces* 2 (2007), 127–140.

p. 117 Gilbert White
Natural History and Antiquities of Selborne, op. cit., letter dated 8 December 1769.

p. 117 'plenty of calories in the sky well into the autumn'
See Tigges: 'The phenology of the Common Swift *Apus apus* in Eurasia and the problem of defining the duration of their stay', op. cit. Edward Jenner got it right. 'Permit me to call to your attention the season at which many of these birds disappear. It happens when they feel no cold blast to benumb them, and when the common food with which they are supported is distributed through the air in great abundance …' 'Some Observations on the Migration of Birds', Philosophical Transactions of the Royal Society, 114 (1824).

p. 119 'Individual birds have their own favourite routes'
A. H. J. Wellbrock, C. Bauch, J. Rozman and K. Witte: '"Same procedure as last year?" Repeatedly tracked swifts show individual consistency in migration pattern in successive years.' *Journal of Avian Biology* 48(6) (2017), 897–903.

p. 120 'African swift populations are organised quite rigidly by reference to latitude'
Susanne Åkesson, Phil W. Atkinson, Ana Bermejo, Javier de la Puente, Mauro Ferri, Chris M. Hewson, Jan Holmgren et al: 'Evolution of chain migration in an aerial insectivorous bird, the Common Swift *Apus apus.*' *Evolution* 74(10) (2020), 2377–2391.

p. 124 'Many Swedish swifts stop in Iberia'
Åkesson et al: 'Migration routes and strategies in a highly aerial migrant, the Common Swift *Apus apus*, revealed by light-level geolocators.' op. cit.

p. 124 'Some Danish swifts arrive in the Sahel on 1 September'
Lars Bo Jacobsen, Niels Odder Jensen, Mikkel Willemoes, Lars Hansen, Mark Desholm, Anthony D. Fox, Anders p. Tøttrup and Kasper Thorup. 'Annual spatiotemporal migration schedules in three larger insectivorous birds: European nightjar, Common Swift and common cuckoo.' *Animal Biotelemetry* 5(1) (2017), 1–11.

p. 124 'The time taken for Swedish swifts to get from Sweden to the border of Niger and Chad'
Åkesson et al: 'Migration routes and strategies in a highly aerial migrant, the Common Swift *Apus apus*, revealed by light-level geolocators.' op. cit.

p. 124 'It's an unhurried journey'
Åkesson et al: 'Migration routes and strategies in a highly aerial migrant, the Common Swift *Apus apus*, revealed by light-level geolocators.' op. cit.

p. 126 'waiting for a tailwind'
Åkesson et al: 'Migration routes and strategies in a highly aerial migrant, the Common Swift *Apus apus*, revealed by light-level geolocators.' op. cit.

p. 128 Aristotle
These are the species usually cited in considerations of Aristotle's theory of bird transformation, but there's real doubt about the identification of them all.

p. 128 'many swallows have been seen in holes'
Aristotle, *History of Animals*, 600a, 10–16, translated by Peter Thonemann.

p. 129 Samuel Johnson
Boswell's *Life of Samuel Johnson*.

p. 129 Gilbert White
Natural History and Antiquities of Selborne, op. cit., Letter to Thomas Pennant.

p. 129 John Hunter
John Hunter, *Essays and Observations on Natural History, Anatomy, Physiology, Psychology and Geology,* Richard Owen (ed), Vol. 2, p. 148, Van Voorst, 1861.

p. 129 'swallows didn't hibernate under water'
See Thomas Pennant's account of this experiment in the *Gentleman's Magazine*, 66, 399 (1796) For an account of changing views on bird migration from antiquity onwards, see I. F. Lyle, 'John Hunter, Gilbert White, and the migration of swallows', Annals of the Royal College of Surgeons of England (1978) 60, 485–491; and Ashleigh

Green, 'Cultural responses to the migration of the barn swallow in Europe' (2019), www.anuhj.com.au.

p. 129 Edward Jenner
'Some Observations on the Migration of Birds', ibid.

p. 130 'metaphysical reasons were almost as conclusive'
ibid.

p. 131 Robert Macfarlane
The Old Ways, Penguin Books, 2012

p. 132 Henry Douglas-Home
The Birdman: Memories of Birds, Collins, 1977, cited Martin Garwood, *The Wind Rippers: Encounters with Swifts* (2019)

p. 135 Thomas Pennant
British Zoology. Vol. 3. W. Eyres, 1776.

p. 135 'always occasional birds around'
There's a reliable UK record on 3 December

p. 136 Bulgaria
Stoyanov, George, and Peter Shurulinkov. 'Late nesting of the Common Swift *Apus apus* and the Pallid Swift Apus pallidus in Bulgaria.' *Acrocephalus* 24, no. 119 (2003): 145–146.

p. 136 'the hippo, Owen, and the Aldabra Giant Tortoise, Mzee'
Craig Hatkoff and Isabella Hatkoff: *Owen and Mzee: The true story of a remarkable friendship*, Scholastic Press, 2006; Isabella Hatkoff, Craig Hatkoff and Paula Kahumbu: *Owen and Mzee: The language of friendship*, Scholastic Press, 2007.

p. 137 'multiplying the number of sensory receptors'
Paul R. Ehrlich, David S. Dobkin and Darryl Wheye: 'Mixed-species flocking' (1988) web.stanford.edu; E. Goodale, p. Ding, X. Liu et al: 'The structure of mixed-species bird flocks, and their response to anthropogenic disturbance, with special reference to East Asia.' *Avian Research* 6, 14 (2015); C. Mammides, J. Chen, U. M. Goodale, S. W. Kotagama and E. Goodale: 'Measurement of species associations in mixed-species bird flocks across environmental and human disturbance gradients.' *Ecosphere* 9(7) (2018): e02324.

p. 137 'structurally more rakish'
Phil Chantler and Gerald Driessens, *Swifts: A Guide to the Swifts and Treeswifts of the World,* Pica Press, 2000, p. 221.

p. 139 'found amongst flocks of pallid swifts along the Nile'
www.birdsoftheworld.org.

p. 140 'the rule is follow the green'
Åkesson et al: 'Evolution of chain migration in an aerial insectivorous bird, the Common Swift *Apus apus*', op. cit.

p. 140 'they eat them in pies'
Swifts have few significant natural predators. They are eaten by the sea, storms and fast and fortunate birds of prey like hobbies. Rats sometimes slink into less cunningly located nests and take nestlings.

p. 140 Tuscany
Cited *Swifts in a Tower,* op. cit., p. 197.

p. 141 Charles Waterton
Cited *Swifts in a Tower,* op. cit., pp. 197–198.

p. 141 'When the temperature suddenly fell in Kent in 1856'
Rev C. A Johns, *British Birds and their Haunts,* George Routledge, 1909, cited *The Wind Rippers,* ibid.

p. 142 Dover
J. M. Harrison, *The Birds of Kent, Vol. 2,* Witherby, cited *The Wind Rippers,* ibid.

p. 142 'industrial farming'
For discussion of toxic residues in swifts, see RobertoMiniero, Claudio Carere, E. De Felip, Nicola Iacovella, Fabrizio Rodriguez, Enrico Alleva, and A. Di Domenico: 'The use of Common Swift (*Apus apus*), an aerial feeder bird, as a bioindicator of persistent organic microcontaminants.' *Annali dell'Istituto superiore di sanita* 44(2) (2008), 187–194.

p. 142 Poznan
J. Zatoński: 'Population of Common Swift in Poznan (Poland) and ecosystem services provided by it.' *Ekonomia i Środowisko* 4 (2016), 263–273.

p. 145 'winter mainly in Namibia and Botswana'
Some also winter in East Africa.

p. 146 'were paler than those of the European swifts'
A. a. pekinensis is also supposed to show 'greater contrast in
wing', according to the Cornell Lab of Ornithology, but I
don't know what that means, and the wings of *A. apus* look
to me to be identical to those of *A. a. pekinensis.*

p. 149 'Recent molecular phylogeny'
Cornell Lab of Ornithology: www.birdsoftheworld.org

p. 151 'southern Europe'
See Oscar Gordo, Juan Jose Sanz and Jorge M Lobo:
'Environmental and geographical constraints on Common
Swift and barn swallow spring migration patterns
throughout the Iberian peninsula.' *Journal of Biogeography*
(2007) 34, 1065–1076; cp Oscar Gordo: 'Does climate
change affect Common Swift *Apus apus* migratory
phenology?' *ApusLife* (2007), 3237.

p. 151 Eurasia
Ulrich Tigges: 'The Phenology of the Common Swift *Apus
apus* in Eurasia and the problem of defining the duration of
their stay', op cit.

p. 151 UK
Stuart E. Newson, Nick J. Moran, Andy J. Musgrove, James
W. Pearce-Higgins, Simon Gillings, Philip W. Atkinson,
Ryan Miller, Mark J. Grantham and Stephen R. Baillie:
'Long-term changes in the migration phenology of UK
breeding birds detected by large-scale citizen science
recording schemes.' *Ibis* 158(3) (2016), 481–495.

p. 151 South Africa
Danni Guo, Gina Zietsman and Philip A. R. Hockey:
'Climate Change Impacts on the Common Swift in South
Africa.' *International Journal of Environmental Science and
Development* 7(4) (2016), 306–311.

Further Reading

There's a sizeable and fast-growing scientific literature on common swifts. Wherever I've relied on a scientific article the citation will be found in an end note. This bibliography only deals with *books* devoted to swifts, and as one might expect, there are few.

The classic text, on which all other consideration of common swifts builds, is David Lack's superb *Swifts in a Tower*. It was originally published in 1956 and had long been out of print before being republished, with an updating chapter written by his son, Andrew Lack, in 2018.

There are only two non-swift-specific books here: Tim Birkhead's great summary of bird senses and Horatio Clare's epic account of his travels along the migration route of a Welsh swallow. Both have a lot to say about the lives of swifts.

Books

Birkhead, Tim, *Bird Sense: What it's like to be a bird*, Bloomsbury Publishing, 2012.

Bromhall, Derek, *Devil Birds: The life of the swift*, Hutchinson, 1980.

Chantler, Phil, *Swifts: A guide to the swifts and treeswifts of the world*, Bloomsbury Publishing, 2010.

Clare, Horatio, *A Single Swallow: Following an epic journey from South Africa to South Wales,* Vintage, 2010.

Garwood, Martin, *The Wind Rippers: Encounters with swifts,* Martin Garwood, 2019.

Glenday J., Summerton R., Lolley A. and Ramsay D, *Swifts,* Salty Press, 2010.

Lack, Andrew and Overall, Roy, *The Museum Swifts*, Oxford University Museum of Natural History, 2002.

Lack, David, *Swifts in a Tower*, Unicorn, 2018.

Pomroy, Jonathan, *On Crescent Wings: A portrait of the swift*, Mascot, 2018.

Unwin, Mike, *RSPB Spotlight: Swifts and Swallows*, Bloomsbury Wildlife, 2018.

Walker, Mark, *Swift Summers: My life with the Common Swift*, Lulu, 2016.

Websites

Common Swift Worldwide is the best first-stop for information on Common Swift biology: **commonswift.org**

Swift Conservation is a treasury of advice about swift conservation, including first aid: **swift-conservation.org**

Action for Swifts is a bulletin board for swift enthusiasts: **actionforswifts.blogspot.com**

The swifts in the Oxford University Tower: **oumnh.ox.ac.uk/swifts-in-the-tower**

The Oxford Swift City project: **rspb.org.uk**

Bristol Swifts: **bristolswifts.co.uk**

SOS Martinets, swift conservation in France: **sosmartinets.com**

Jochem Kuhnen, a Dutch Common Swift enthusiast: **xjochemx.nl**

BTO swift tracking project: **bto.org**

Jonathan Pomroy, wildlife artist, specialising in swifts, and the illustrator of this book: **jonathanpomroy.wordpress.com**

Acknowledgements

Writing the acknowledgments is always a happy but frustrating part of writing any book. Happy, because you're forced to remember convivial evenings and thrilling trips and enlightening conversations and generosity and encouragement. And frustrating, because a few words, or the mere mention of a name, are so inadequate a recompense for all the time, hospitality, patience and wisdom, and because there are always so many people who wrongly don't even get the mention.

In no particular order, very many thanks to:

Amnonn Hahn, who flies amongst the swifts in his paraglider, and who has been an extraordinary, energetic and inspired champion of swifts in Israel.

Professor Susanne Akesson, of Lund University, Sweden, whose work with geolocators and GPS devices has revolutionised our understanding of common swift migration.

Professor Andy Gosler, of the Department of Zoology, University of Oxford, who took me up the swift tower in the Oxford University Museum.

Ulrich Tigges, whose passion for swifts led to the

convening of the International Swift conferences and to the creation of the superb resource which is commonswift.org. I'm particularly grateful to him for discussion of the notion of the territory of breeding colonies.

Dr Nir Sapir, of the Animal Flight Group at the University of Haifa, for a preview of his findings about the migration routes of Israeli swifts.

Lyndon Kearsley, whose tracking of swifts in Belgium is helping to answer some fundamental questions about the behaviour of breeding swifts.

Chris Mason, acute and visionary protector of Oxfordshire's swifts.

Professor Peter Thonemann, for kind but rigorous interrogation of my presumptions about swift biology, and for his translation of Aristotle.

Dr Chris Thouless, who has taught me more than anyone else about how African ecosystems hang together.

Mark McCullins, chief test pilot at Airbus, who has flown the swifts' migration routes to and from Africa hundreds of times, and who made the sky live for me.

Everyone at the International Swift Conferences. I've learned so much from you.

Over the years I've had wonderful hospitality from hundreds of people in many African, Asian and European countries as I've mooched around on the track of swifts. Thank you all.

Many friends have shaped my understanding of the natural world, including David Abram, John Butler, Rachel Campbell-Johnston, Peter and Laura Carew, John and Margaret Cooper, James Crowden, Steve Ely, John and Nicki Fletcher, Mariam Motamedi Fraser, Jay Griffiths, David Haskell, Caspar Henderson, Ben Hill, Marie Hauge

Jensen, Helen Jukes, Paul Kingsnorth, Andy Letcher, John Lister-Kaye, Iain McGilchrist, George Monbiot, Helen Mort, Nigel and Janet Phillips, Jill Purce, Colin Roberts, Karl Segnoe, Martin Shaw, Cosmo Sheldrake, Merlin Sheldrake, Rupert Sheldrake, Katherine Stathatou, Colin Tudge, Mark and Sue West, Ruth West and Derek Whiteley.

I'm so grateful to Adrian Cooper, Gracie Burnett, Jon Woolcott and Graham Shackleton at Little Toller for believing in this book, and, as ever, to my brilliant agent and friend Jessica Woollard for all her inspiration, understanding and hard graft.

As soon as I saw Jonathan Pomroy's work I knew that I wanted him to illustrate this book. He understands better than anyone else how swifts move One of the many points of real genius in the cover picture is the juxtaposition of the low-level vegetation and the top of the roof. It's thrillingly disorienting and vertiginous, and gives the impression that swifts occupy a different *kind* of space – which of course they do. If the book is judged by its cover I'll be delighted. Jonathan also read the book in draft and put me right on some important points of swift biology.

I've admitted in this book how guilty I feel that I've given the swifts time that my wonderful and long-suffering family should have had. Mary, Tom, Jamie, Rachel and Jonny: I'm very sorry, and very grateful that you put up with me.

C. F.
Oxford, 2021